# Festina Lente

Henry Rollin (portrait by Jacob Kramer, 1952)

HENRY R ROLLIN

# Festina Lente

## A Psychiatric Odyssey

The
MEMOIR
Club

The British Medical Journal
Tavistock Square, London WC1H 9JR

First published 1990

ISBN 0 7279 0285 7

The quotation from T S Eliot's poem "The Love Song of J Alfred Prufrock" is
reproduced from *T S Eliot: Collected Poems 1909–1962* by permission of Faber and
Faber Ltd.

Typeset in Great Britain by Latimer Trend & Co. Ltd, Plymouth
Printed in Great Britain by The University Press, Cambridge

For Maria

# Acknowledgments

Somewhere at the back of my consciousness, and for a very long time, has lurked the intention of writing what is tantamount to my memoirs. What is virtually certain, however, is that they would never have been written had not Stephen Lock spurred my intent with his generous and wholly unexpected invitation to join the Memoir Club. To him, therefore, I must give thanks – and in plenty.

I am indebted beyond all measure to my secretary, Mrs Diana Shields. For more years than I (or she) would care to remember she has uncomplainingly put up with my infuriating way of writing, or rather rewriting, which for her has meant typing and retyping one draft after another. For the purposes of this book she has gone even further and with her customary panache has solved the riddles of the word processor, riddles which for complexity make those posed by the Princess Turandot to her suitors the merest child's play. My sole contribution to the whole miraculous process has been to sit and gawk at the machine as it spewed out what had begun as my scrawled manuscript into ream upon ream of elegant typescript.

The manuscript has been gone through with a fine toothcomb by my sternest critic, my wife Maria, who, apart from making many valuable suggestions, has saved me from the ignominy of more than a few grammatical and syntactical errors. My thanks too to Dea Forsdyke (Lady Forsdyke) who, as so often in the past, has acted as proof-reader in chief.

As I have indicated in the prologue, the task of compiling this book has been made that much easier by being able to refer to to my previous publications, from which I have "borrowed" extensively. I would, however, like to acknowledge formally and with thanks permission to reproduce material which has appeared in the *British Medical Journal*, the *Lancet*, the *Journal of the Royal Society of Medicine*, the *British Journal of Psychiatry*, the *Practitioner*, *World Medicine*, the *University of Leeds Review*, the *Cambridge Review*, *Psychological Medicine*, the *Transactions of the College of Medicine of Philadelphia*, and the *Nursing Mirror*.

# Contents

I have measured out my life with coffee spoons.
T S ELIOT, *The Love Song of J Alfred Prufrock*

# Prologue

It has been my singular good fortune to have been allowed to translate my thoughts into print for well nigh half a century – even longer if I were to take into account contributions to school and undergraduate publications. The latter, like so much of the ephemera of my childhood and youth, have been lost or destroyed – a loss which only someone misguided enough to wish to write my biography would mourn.

However, since I became reconciled to becoming a doctor, and, indeed, began actually to enjoy the practice of medicine, or more precisely, psychiatry, I have collected and indexed my publications in an almost obsessive manner. In my time I have covered the entire medical journalist's gamut from books and original papers through leading articles and book reviews to "letters to the editor". What has delighted me particularly has been the privilege of contributing to the non-technical, non-medical columns of the *British Medical Journal* and the *Lancet*. I refer of course to the Personal View and Materia non Medica columns of the former and the Peripatetic Correspondents column of the latter. As a vehicle for such literary jeux d'esprit I would mention with special affection *World Medicine* which, during its too short life, encouraged its contributors to give free rein to their literary inventiveness and to their talent for writing in a lighter vein.

Writing as much as I have done, and, what is more, collecting so assiduously what I have written, was never part of a conscious Grand Design. Nevertheless, whatever the motivation, conscious or unconscious, neurotic or otherwise, the task of writing this book has been made that much easier by being able to draw on my files. Some of the items here included are reproduced in their entirety and their source and the permission to do so duly acknowledged. In some instances I have elaborated on what I have previously written, and where necessary I have done my utmost to check dates and place names as thoroughly as I can.

It has been my earnest intent to be as truthful as I know how, although on occasion a combination of reticence and discretion has prevented me from telling the whole truth.

Throughout these chapters I have used real names. There are two exceptions, namely, the medical superintendent of Caterham Hospital and the group captain at RAF Little Rissington who was responsible for my precipitate posting. For both these men I have a positive loathing, a feeling which I have no doubt was mutual. Rather than invent fictitious names I have chosen to leave them nameless. I have ascertained that neither is in the land of the living, but I am sufficiently charitable now to wish both of them well – wherever they may be.

What has been included between these boards is in no way an autobiography. I prefer to regard it essentially as a history of psychiatry during the past half century as seen by one who has been witness to and played some small part in the shaping of events, events of such moment as to have elevated the status of psychiatry from the fourth to the first division in the ranks of medical specialties. Nevertheless, the credibility of witnesses needs to be established, and it is with this end in view that I have included, particularly in the first chapter, "Early stages", a broad outline of the influences responsible for the sort of person I have become. I do not believe that a man is necessarily master of his fate, but I do believe most sincerely that he can conspire with fate to make the best of what is available within himself.

# 1 Early stages

It is a sobering thought that, if Latin had been included in my clutch of credits when I matriculated, I might today have been a retired schoolmaster, or whatever a modest degree from a provincial university would have fitted me for. My interests were, and if truth be told, have continued to be, in the arts. Since childhood I have been awed by the power and beauty of language and have sweetly savoured the subtlety of words. I have read voraciously – an activity encouraged by my father, one of nature's scholars, himself an historian, bibliophile, and linguist. Every nook and cranny of every house we ever lived in he filled with books in English, Russian, Yiddish, and Hebrew – languages he spoke and wrote fluently. There was the odd book too in Esperanto, which his firmly held belief in International Socialism convinced him would be the lingua franca of the Utopia to come. In addition, room had to be found for his real pride and joy, his very considerable and valuable collection of documents and memorabilia, now deposited with Warwick University, concerned with the early history of socialism and trade unions, particularly Jewish trade unions. Scholarship almost literally oozed from our walls and I would have had to be an insensitive brute not to have absorbed a liking of it by a process of something akin to osmosis.

Leeds, where I spent my formative years, had at least one redeeming feature: it boasted in those days a host of theatres including the Royal and the Grand, both deserving of their splendid names, and both considered eminently suitable for productions on their way to or from London. For a modest sixpence I had access to the best the English theatre had to offer, and there can have been few established or rising stars who have not fallen within my gaze from my position of vantage in the "gods". I remember, for example, circa 1930, a presentation of *Private Lives*, the cast of which included the playwright, Noel Coward lui-même, Laurence Olivier, Adrianne Allen, and Gertrude Lawrence, and I recall drooling with delight as these magicians conjured a ton of entertainment out of an ounce of dramatic puff-pastry. Of comparable brilliance was the performance of Charles Laughton as Tony Perelli, the Al Capone-like gangster, in Edgar Wallace's *On the Spot*, a performance which many have tried, but none has succeeded in emulating. And all for sixpence!

If I was endowed with any talent at all it was as a writer. I can hardly remember a time when I failed to feel an involuntary tingle of excitement tinged with apprehension when faced with a blank sheet of foolscap. Not that writing comes easily: I am too obsessional for that, so that anything I have ever written has been subjected to many drafts and continued revision. It was this quirk, incidentally, ignorance apart, which militated against the completion in time of any written examination I have ever sat.

But it was Latin, or the absence thereof, that did me down. No Latin, no admission to the Faculty of Arts. What then was the alternative? My father, noble soul that he was, had always wanted me to be a doctor, a profession he saw to be honourable and compatible with his decidedly left wing political views. I was finally persuaded; and with minimal enthusiasm I enrolled at the age of 16 in the Faculty of Medicine of Leeds University in 1928.

At best I was an indifferent student, not because I was particularly dim, but because I had not the slightest interest in what I was called upon to study. There was not a single subject in the curricula for the first or second MB examinations that appealed to my heart or mind. Rote learning, that painful acquisition of knowledge without thinking, was anathema to me. There was no scope for what I, pompously maybe, considered to be the very essence of a university, namely, the right to challenge one's teachers, or to think differently.

But the Rubicon had been crossed. The financial investment in me was too great for me even to contemplate a switch in direction. I worked – when I worked – without inspiration and without joy. I managed to maintain my equilibrium, however, by my extra-curricular activities. My devotion to the theatre had continued, but to this I had added music and the opera – all, that is, within the constraints of my meagre weekly allowance. I kept abreast of contemporary literature but found myself more and more seduced by American writers, particularly by that incomparable galaxy of humorists, Don Marquis, Damon Runyon, James Thurber, and S J Perelman. My debt to Mr Perelman, incidentally, is substantially enhanced in the knowledge that he is responsible for some of the scripts of the Marx Brothers, who became a cult of which I remain an unashamed votary.

Life took on a somewhat rosier complexion when clinical work began. I was intrigued (and still am) by the problems of clinical diagnosis which, for their solution, demand the joint talents of a craftsman, an historian, and, fortunately, for me only minimally those of a scientist.

I qualified in 1935, not all that late in fact, but the most assiduous of researchers would fail to find my name on any honours board, or in any list of prizemen. It could, however, be found in small print in the cast list of gentlemen of the chorus in various university theatrical productions and as the author of occasional contributions to university undergraduate publications. Writ in much larger type on some board somewhere is my name as lightweight boxing champion in 1932–3 of both Leeds and the Northern Universities, (the "Christie" Champion).

I have often been asked why I took up boxing, which in so many ways would appear to be incompatible with my other major interests. I suppose the answer is that I have always had to fight my corner. This was particularly so as a boy in Leeds where I differed from the herd on two counts. Firstly, I was a Jew, one of a tiny minority in an overwhelmingly lower middle class, Christian community. Antisemitic taunts were few and far between, but when they did come, as inevitably they must, I would fly at my tormentor with uncontrolled fury, delivering bludgeoning blows with arms and legs. At that time I had never heard of the Queensberry Rules and would have disregarded them even if I had. Sometimes I won my fights, more often I lost, for the simple reason that bullies tend to be physically large and I was small for my age (my nickname was "Titch").

The other difference which occasionally provoked a scrap was one far less likely to involve a pre-pubescent child of whatever religious denomination – politics. Ours was a staunchly Conservative constituency. My father, as I have already indicated, was a dedicated socialist. My older sister Ethel and I attended a socialist Sunday school a goodly distance from our home where the aim was unashamedly political, not religious, indoctrination. We joined in the May Day parades, at one of which my sister was May Queen. And, in order to advertise our difference from the rest even more explicitly, ours was the only house in the street (ironically overlooking the bowling green of the local Conservative Club) to carry, at the time of the elections, posters in support of the Labour candidate – a minute oasis of Labour red in a desert of Tory blue.

The family fortunes at the time I qualified were at their lowest ebb and the immediate imperative was to earn money. In those days there was no legal obligation to do post-qualification house jobs, but I felt morally obliged to augment my scant student experience with some work in hospital. The General Infirmary at Leeds paid its housemen nothing beyond their keep, not that I had a cat in hell's chance of being appointed to the house, taking into account my track record as a student and the anything but covert antisemitic policy then pursued. But I did succeed in getting a job at the Oldham Royal Infirmary which served my purpose excellently; and it did pay its housemen, albeit modestly.

Housemen then, at least in small provincial hospitals, worked inordinately hard. There were no set hours and only one half day off duty a week, and that more often than not was honoured in the breach. Even the wee hours of the morning when ordinary folk were abed were far from sacrosanct. We were at the mercy of local GPs, some genuinely anguished, some of them not. I remember being awakened

4

from a deep and well earned sleep by the telephone.

"This is Dr Brown from Failsworth speaking," said the unapologetic voice at the other end. "I've got a baby here – screaming!" I can't remember precisely what my reply was, but I doubt if it was particularly polite.

On another occasion I was awakened, not this time by the telephone, but by the awareness that the light over my bed had been switched on. The intruder turned out to be the night porter, a good friend of mine, who saw it as his duty to protect "his doctors" from unnecessary nocturnal intrusions and interruptions.

"I'm right sorry, Mr Rollin," he apologised in his unmistakable Lancastrian accent, "I know you've had a bloody awful day, but you see it's a BID and the police is waiting to get it certified dead."

I made to get out of bed but he gently pushed me back.

"There's no need to get up, I've brought it with me."

At this he wheeled in a trolley and flung back a red blanket to reveal an unfortunate suicide whose mangled remains had been scraped off the railway lines a mile or two from the hospital.

After Oldham, what? Specialisation requiring higher qualifications was out of the question for a variety of reasons, not the least of which was my low self-esteem, academically speaking at any rate. To tide things over, locums in hospitals, both general and mental, or in general practice, were fairly readily available. So for a time I wandered the country as a medical gypsy, using the family home – by then in London – as a base. I learnt little psychiatry as such in my wanderings, but what I did learn was that medical officers in mental hospitals were not overworked, and, furthermore, that they enjoyed generous time off and an inordinately high standard of living.

My experience of general practice was extraordinarily varied and ranged from mercifully short locums in sweatshop practices in the East End of London to one lasting several months in a smart West End practice, which offered the use of an elegant flat to boot. The added attraction of this particular job was that included among the list of patients were several employed in the theatre, through whose good offices I could go to as many matinées as I had time for, or to evening performances when the house needed a little "papering".

It was through this particular practice that I met James Agate, the leading dramatic critic of the time, and it was in his exalted company that I was privileged to attend several "first nights". Despite his fame, or perhaps because of it, Agate was without doubt the most unpleasant man I have ever known. He was arrogantly conceited, bigoted, overweening, imperious, unreliable, disloyal, untrustworthy, and perverse in every sense of that multifaceted word. And yet despite this catalogue of undesirable personality traits he was, again without doubt, the most fascinating man I have ever known, a fascination which lay primarily in his wit, and in his innate sense of theatre. He was a consummate actor, and to be in his company was to be seated centre stalls at a private, highly professional, one-man show. He was, in fact, never off stage and never gave a bad performance.

As an example of his scintillating wit, spiced with his characteristic bitchiness, I would cite the following poem composed, he says, while he was shaving one morning:

Mister Korda
Sent for Lord Horder
Because of the strictures
People pass on his pictures!

Agate cultivated controversy. He was never happier than when he was at daggers drawn with some opponent, particularly the Inland Revenue. He concludes his own obituary fittingly: "His enemies will miss him." But so will a host of friends.

Whether of high or low degree, I had become convinced that general practice of the one-man sort was unmitigated drudgery and/or slavery and not to my liking although, on reflection, an alternative was difficult to visualise.

I felt cornered: and it was then that I decided to throw discretion to the winds and to engage in an act of inexcusable self-indulgence. I applied for, and within a week was offered, an appointment with the Blue Funnel Line as a ship's surgeon. So it was that towards the end of 1937 I sailed from Birkenhead in the MV *Memnon* on a voyage lasting six months, calling at ports strung like precious jewels halfway round the world to Japan and back, ports of call which hitherto had seemed as inaccessible as the topmost peaks of the Himalayas. In almost every way I was exceedingly fortunate. These were the last days of a dying empire; but the going was still good and an old pound sterling would still buy one and a half white drill suits made to measure in 24 hours in Singapore, exquisite silks in trashy wrappings in Shanghai, and trashy silks in exquisite wrappings in Yokohama. My pay was £10 a month – far from princely even by pre-1939 standards – but to this must be added first class accommodation and the exclusive services of a Chinese "boy" who saw his home in Hong Kong once a year, just long enough to greet his last child and start another.

The surgery, the domain over which I reigned supreme, measured about 12 feet by 4 feet. The antibiotic revolution had not yet taken place, so that by the standards of today my medications were simple if not downright rudimentary. They were contained in four large winchesters labelled in order, Mist Alba, Mist Alkali, Mist Expect Stim and Mist Expect Sed. To accommodate those with less than a first class honours degree in medicine the labels were further inscribed, "For the Bowels", "For the Stomach", "For the Dry Cough", and "For the Wet Cough".

The surgical equipment was equally sparse, but in the event, adequate for what I was called on to do. By far the most frequently used instruments were the upper and lower universal dental forceps I had borrowed from a dentist friend. The engine crew were Chinese to a man, and they, I came to learn, had the most appalling teeth and gums. They presented themselves one after another with toothache and indicated by sign language – the only means of communication – that they wished the offending tooth (or teeth) to be extracted. This I did; and in cold steel. This may appear callous, even barbaric, but the tooth (or teeth) were invariably so loose that the minimum force was required to extract them. Even so, I had distinct qualms as a surgeon-dentist extraordinary; but these were assuaged somewhat by the thought that in my absence ashore my deputy was Chippie, the ship's carpenter, who relied – if the occasion arose – on tools peculiar to his craft.

From a purely professional standpoint the voyage was unadulterated lotus-eating, but no matter what guilt feelings I allowed myself to entertain at the time I would not, in retrospect, have missed the exotic experience, an experience so rich that it has fuelled my imagination ever since. Not only this, but it sparked off a positive lust for travel, a lust which has thus far proved insatiable.

# 2 Apprentice psychiatrist

I wish I could say that my choice of psychiatry as a specialty was determined by some inner, irresistible, driving force. Certainly I drew no inspiration from the undergraduate teaching in psychiatry I had received. This had consisted of half a dozen deadly dull lectures given by the distinguished, but by now aged, Professor Shaw Bolton on neuropathology and cortical histology, which he proceeded to illustrate with slides. The lights were switched off in the lecture theatre and in the ensuing darkness his students either fell peacefully asleep or slipped out quietly and unobtrusively. Then, in mid-term, we were transported by bus to Wakefield Asylum (Stanley Royd Hospital as it now is). There a handful of patients, mainly chronic hypomanics and all of them experienced entertainers, went through their paces in what was tantamount to a well drilled music hall show. A sumptuous tea was then served, a fair sample of the standard fare available to medical staff in mental hospitals at that time. And so ended the first – and only – lesson in the art of clinical psychiatry.

No, what drove me to psychiatry was nothing less than dire necessity. I was weary of the fragmented, structureless life of the locum. I needed a job with continuity and responsibility. I even applied for the post of assistant medical officer to the GPO and remember being interviewed in a musty, dingy room at the Post Office in London by a musty, dingy senior medical officer and hoping against hope that I would not be appointed. I wasn't; but it was still humiliating.

An advertisement appeared in the *BMJ* in late 1938 for assistant medical officers in the London County Council Mental Hospitals Department. I was not slow to realise that such a job offered not only a career structure, but for me, hedonist that I am, the additional advantages of proximity to London and a standard of living I had only sampled in my previous wanderings. I applied, and to my intense relief, was appointed.

The hospitals controlled in those days by the London County Council Mental Hospitals Department ringed the metropolis like a bicycle wheel, with County Hall, the administrative power house, at the hub, and the Maudsley Hospital, the think-tank, a little off centre. All together they provided a mental health service which, despite its rigid social stratification and its religious devotion to the book of rules, was efficient, prestigious, powerful, and as eternal as Imperial Rome.

The medical staffing structure was hierarchical. In shape it was like an inverted ice-cream cone, or, better still, a steep-sided mountain with, at intervals, camps where the weary climber could rest or even dig in during the arduous ascent to the summit. At its foot, learning the ropes, were the assistant medical officers allocated to a particular hospital after their appointment to the Mental Health Service. How this allocation was made remains shrouded in mystery, but rumour had it that the least promising appointees were posted to what were then called mental deficiency hospitals. I was posted to a mental deficiency hospital – to wit, Caterham Hospital as it was known before it was canonised and became St Lawrence's Hospital.

Assistant medical officers were in all respects probationers. Retention in the service beyond three years was – and I quote from a letter still in my possession dated February, 1939, and signed by the chief officer, "Imperial Caesar" himself – "conditional upon your securing a degree or diploma in psychological medicine and upon the submission of a definite report by the medical superintendent that you have shown yourself entirely suitable for consideration in due course for promotion," etc. Only perfection could measure up to the requirements of this masterpiece of bureaucratic cunning. The threat, therefore, that the medical superintendent might choose not to submit such a report hung constantly over our heads like the sword of Damocles. The rule vis-à-vis the Diploma in Psychological Medicine (DPM) was mercilessly applied. Those who failed slipped quietly away and were heard of no more – except, that is, for a few erstwhile colleagues who dropped in now and again, well heeled and smug, having made the "big time" elsewhere with indecent haste and without the aid of academic safety nets.

Those who succeeded were rewarded with a cash bonus of £50 a year and the privilege of attempting the next stage, to second assistant medical officer. This was not all that difficult although, in circumstances which I will later explain, I failed at the first attempt. There were those whose ambition petered out at this point, so that once secure in a job which provided sufficient bread and a little cake they were content to dig in as "chronic seconds" and play out time until death or a pension overtook them. The mental hospital had supplied them with what they most needed for themselves – an asylum. For those, however, sounder in wit, wind, and limb, the climb went on up to the dizzy heights of first assistant medical officer, then deputy superintendent, and finally through clouds of improbability, to the sunlit summit, to medical superintendent.

Though not actually written down in the imperial edict, it was generally acknowledged that the handmaiden of success was the possession of higher qualifications. As early as possible in the struggle upwards further blood, sweat, and tears were poured out to convert MBs into MDs and the Ls of LRCPs into Ms. There were some scholastic gluttons who achieved both. The relevance to psychiatry of such medical degrees and diplomas seemed obvious, but I was puzzled as to the relevance of the FRCS, Eng, or Ed, which was the sole higher qualification of a few. Or was it that Caesar's soothsayer foretold the advent (if not the perils) of the era of "psychosurgery", and he in his infinite wisdom was, as always, prepared?

The medical superintendents were the proconsuls of this great psychiatric empire. Symbols of their power and prestige abounded. They alone, apart from substantial "perks" that went with the job, broke the financial sound barrier of £1000 a year – and in those days you doffed your cap, no matter what, to a "four-figure man". They maintained, or were maintained in, huge establishments, and it would appear that a goodly proportion of the occupational therapy of the time was concerned with making life fit for living for these "super" men. A weed left in their private, immaculately manicured, tennis lawn by some careless helot was a crime punishable with unmentionable penalties.

Not that we underlings, the assistant medical officers, did too badly. We were fed like fighting cocks, and were waited on hand and foot in our own quarters by uniformed male servants. Our shoes shone like black diamonds, and our personal linen, hand-laundered, gleamed whiter than white. Our rooms showed the same devotion and pride in a job well done; the unseen hands that cleaned and polished had the Midas touch, visibly capable of transmuting the ubiquitous base brass into glittering gold.

Privilege of this sort had its price, a price exacted not so much in the cost of our board and lodging – which was modest enough, not in the routine work – which was light enough, but in the unnecessary and insufferable incursions into our personal and private lives.

A bachelor medical officer was obliged to live in, and by "live in" was meant to sleep in, even if he was not on duty, unless permission to do otherwise had been sought from the medical superintendent and graciously granted. Twice I sinned against this canon and twice I was carpeted. I, of course, refused either to explain my conduct or to apologise. He could think what he liked, I said, knowing full well what he thought, and knowing equally well that what he thought was absolutely correct.

But we were not the only ones to suffer; the same heavy hand was felt right down the line to the most recently joined ward maid who needed the job, and who may have waited months to get it.

The book of rules which governed all the lives of all grades of staff incorporated a paragraph or two from some hallowed text on Victorian morality and allowed room also for an occasional footnote, inserted locally, from the teachings of Calvin. In our society there were no men and no women; there were only "members of the opposite sex". Courting couples – that is to say, opposite members of the opposite sex – had to carry on their courtship outside the hospital or its grounds. Cerberus, guardian of the infernal gates, was never so watchful as our gate porter, always ready to note down and report later any backward glance, any holding of hands, or any stolen kiss once the threshold had been crossed.

But if the terms of appointment and conditions of service of medical officers were somewhat idiosyncratic, so too were those of nurses, particularly males. An appointment to the staff of a mental hospital could depend on whether there was a need for a left full-back, a spin bowler, a middle-distance runner, or a second trombone. At first glance this would appear to be a singularly capricious and arbitrary method of selection, but if seen in the context of the times it did make some sort of sense. Mental hospitals pre-1939 were in effect total institutions: the patient population was relatively static; security was tight and, as a result, contact with the outside world was tenuous to say the least. This pattern applied just as much to "mental deficiency" hospitals as it did to the mental hospitals. What entertainment there was had to be provided largely by the staff. Ostensibly, then, the hospital football and cricket teams, the athletics squad, and the band were there as a means to entertain the patients. But the means very frequently became an end in themselves. The success of the teams became a symbol of prestige to all concerned, and to win an important inter-hospital competition might well be the high water mark of the career of a medical superintendent.

So it was that in an era when jobs were hard to come by sportsmen and bandsmen had an edge on others not so endowed. There were not a few ex-professional footballers, minor county cricketers, and proud possessors of England, even Olympic, vests who were glad to join an honourable profession which, as an added bonus, gave them splendid facilities to continue to exploit their primary talents. The band too had its professionals. There had always been a steady flow into the hospitals of time-served soldiers, some of whom had trained at Kneller Hall, that renowned army academy of music. And if it happened, as sometimes it did, that a man was blessed with a nifty embouchure and nimble feet to boot then to him the paths to the topmost peaks of his adopted profession were wide open. Not that, I hasten to add, there was necessarily an incompatibility between these natural aptitudes and the compassionate care of patients. Good sportsmen and good musicians could, and more often than not did, make excellent mental nurses.

Dances played a most important role in the entertainment programme of both patients and staff. The patients' dances were characterised by the separation of the sexes: those of the staff were characterised by the separation of the social classes. At both, the hospital band officiated – and very well too.

The patients' dances, at which an assistant medical officer was obliged to be present throughout, were held once a week in the great hall, a vast auditorium large enough to house a fleet of jumbo jets but with acoustics that had to be heard, or rather, not heard, to be believed. The men patients were ranged down one side of the hall, the women down the other. The bandmaster, an ex-guardsman, wore his flamboyant Ruritanian uniform as to the manner born. In a stentorian voice, more suited to the parade ground than to the ballroom, he gave the command, "Take your partners for a waltz" (or a valeta, a military two-step, or whatever). And take their partners they did. As though guided by automatic pilot each man shambled across the crowded floor towards his target – his partner of the previous dance, of the previous week, of the previous year, or years. They rarely spoke, and irrespective of the rhythm or tempo of the music they went through the same grotesque gyrations: it was the fleeting intimacy that counted, even amongst those who were not only intellectually retarded, but for the most part clumsy, if not physically disabled.

The best pen-picture of what took place during these brief encounters is painted by Lewis Carroll in the Lobster Quadrille: ". . . and the two creatures, who had been jumping about like mad things all this time, sat down again very sadly and quietly and looked . . ." It was indeed sad, if one stopped to think, that after the traditional last waltz to end the evening's entertainment, there would be no more close contact with a fellow human being for another week.

14

For the staff, dances, although not assuming the same importance as they did for the patients, were nevertheless high water marks in the social calendar. We, the medical officers, bedecked in white ties, formed the core of an élite group, "the platform party" – so called because it occupied the platform, thus ousting the band from its rightful place, and at the same time demonstrating our elevation above and separation from the common herd that thronged the floor below. Centre stage sat the medical superintendent with his lady. He hated dances as in truth he hated almost everything. He found dances a bore, and in this respect he had every justification. They were a bore; a crashing bore. A bachelor, and such was I in those days, came unaccompanied and served as a spare man, obliged by courtesy rather than inclination, to partner ladies who enjoyed the same doubtful privilege of belonging to the platform party. To do otherwise would have been unthinkable and unpardonable.

There was one break in this too, too solid class wall – a Paul Jones. By tradition we were permitted to descend from our Olympian heights and join in this ballroom roulette. Theoretically a Paul Jones is a game of chance, but the odds can be materially shortened by a little skulduggery so that when the counter-revolving circles come to stop, one can be eyeball-to-eyeball with a "member of the opposite sex" somewhat fairer of face and lighter of foot than our prescribed partners. We too, therefore, had our fleeting moments of contact with love objects, made the more desirable because they were so rigorously forbidden.

A certain authenticity is given to my account of these gala events in a letter, dated 7 May 1972, from the ex-secretary of our medical superintendent. She had seen me a night or two before in a *Panorama* programme on television and had written to me. Recalling life at Caterham at precisely this time she writes, inter alia: "There is one incident which came to my mind about the staff dances, because one night the great panjandrum had come down from his Olympian heights to rub shoulders with his people of low degree, and the Paul Jones stopped and he was face to face with a young probationer. She turned deadly white and gasped, 'Oh my God'. I think that summed up the situation neatly."

The influence of medical superintendents on the career prospects of junior doctors cannot be exaggerated. In my case, at Caterham, as my readers will have gathered, my fate rested in the hands of an ignorant, pig-headed bigot whose sole claim to psychiatric distinction lay in the possession of the FRCSEd, to the possible relevance of which I have already referred. I was fully aware of the jeopardy in which I had placed myself by my open hostility towards him, but my self-esteem would not permit me to act otherwise, although I realised that in these brushes with authority could lie the reason why I was considered not "entirely suitable for consideration in due course for promotion". Indeed, there was one occasion in 1940 when I applied for the job as a "second" which had fallen vacant in the hospital. I failed to be appointed, although it was generally agreed by my colleagues that justice had not been exactly even-handed.

Fortunately for me, the said FRCSEd showed not the slightest interest, and took no part, in the clinical work of the hospital. This he left to his deputy, Charles James Cecil Earl, a bachelor who had rooms in the hospital, and who served as Mess president. Earl was the first of a long string of teachers of first class importance who took an interest in me and who, singly and together, have had such a profound influence on my career.

Earl was a remarkable man. He was a patrician Dubliner who fitted well into the upper crust mould of the Savile Club, to which he was elected soon after his translation to London. From time to time he would invite me to dine at his club, occasions which were for me gala events, albeit somewhat intimidating for one so young and so unaccustomed to grandeur of that order. He exacted a small payment for these treats: we travelled together to London by Green Line (fare 1s 7d return) and I was enjoined to keep awake so as to be able to rouse him from his alcoholised slumbers when the bus stopped at the hospital gates which, most conveniently, it did.

Earl was a brilliant raconteur and wit. He did not suffer fools gladly. (These attributes could be combined, and never more brilliantly than the occasion when presiding at dinner one night he reflected that the only time our worthy medical superintendent saw a defective was when he shaved in the morning.) He was also unusual in that he had deliberately chosen to work in the field of mental deficiency rather than, as was more often the case, having gravitated into it on a faute-de-mieux basis. He was recognised, inter alia, as an international authority on intelligence tests and projective techniques, particularly in relation to those who were then termed "feeble minded" and with personality problems. His specialty was the now outmoded Rorschach test, into the intricacies of the scoring of which he tried to indoctrinate me – with singularly little success, I'm afraid.

As far as I was personally concerned, however, his most important attribute was his iconoclasm: he loved taking pot shots at revered idols, and the more revered the better. He took kindly, therefore, to my iconoclastic observation that of the 73 mongols (that is how they were then termed) in our hospital, singularly few conformed to the accepted description of their personality characteristics as portrayed by Dr J Langdon Down in 1866, a description which had been handed down unchallenged from one textbook to another. For example, in A F Tredgold's *Text Book of Mental Deficiency*, 6th edition, 1937, a mongol is described as "of happy and cheerful disposition; he is affectionate, good tempered, and easily amused; he likes to be taken notice of and he is usually a great favourite with all who have to do with him. The mongol may be mischievous and given to childish pranks but it is rare to find him guilty of bad temper or any of the vices or bad habits which characterise so many of the ordinary defective." Not only did the majority of our mongols fail to measure up to this charming pen-picture, but it seemed to me that a considerable proportion, particularly those in the lowest intellectual categories, were by any standards psychotic and approximated to a syndrome first described by Earl himself as "Primitive catatonic psychosis". Earl readily agreed that this was a worthwhile subject for investigation and encouraged me to have a go. Not only this, but the University of Leeds, when presented with a synopsis of my proposed research, accepted it

17

as a fitting subject for a thesis which, if of sufficient merit, would make a substantial contribution towards the award of the MD degree. I had perforce to ask the permission of the superintendent to go ahead. His response was entirely predictable.

"How much is it going to cost?", he asked.

"Not a penny", I replied.

There were no grounds other than financial that could cause him to object so he grunted his approval.

Even to this day I can recall the tingle of excitement the letter of acceptance by the university created. The year was 1939. The war clouds gathering over Europe were becoming blacker and blacker – not the most propitious setting for a research programme which, on the face of it, had not the slightest relevance to the momentous events outside the hospital which threatened to destroy the very fabric of civilisation. But, surprisingly perhaps, I asked and was granted the full cooperation of my colleagues, the nursing staff, and the ancillary staff. I say "surprisingly", because in mid-1939 part of the hospital had been handed over to the Emergency Medical Service (EMS) and a corresponding number of our patients had to be transferred to other hospitals. In spite of the upheaval, however, I not only began, but when all hell broke loose during the Blitzkrieg, pressed on and managed to complete what I had set out to do before, in June 1941, I decided that enough was enough and symbolically beat my ploughshare (or Koh's Blocks) into a sword and went off to fight the foe. I submitted my thesis, "Personality in mongolism with special reference to the incidence of catatonic psychosis", to the university explaining that in the circumstances I must postpone the completion of the examination sine die. Some time later they informed me that my thesis had been accepted and asked if I would let them know when I was ready to present myself for the rest of the examination. A paper based on my thesis was published in the *American Journal of Mental Deficiency* in 1946, however.[1]

It would be difficult to exaggerate the psychological importance of the work I did on my 73 mongols, each and every one of whom I came to know intimately and with whom, degraded and depraved as some of them were, I formed a close attachment. For the first time, professionally speaking, I had acquired a raison-d'être.

## DOCTOR CHARLOTTE WOLFF

It was at the time that I was busy with my mongols that Dr Charlotte Wolff, a very strange lady indeed, erupted into our midst. Her dark, straight hair was severely bobbed: she wore a tailor-made costume and a collar and tie, leaving no doubt that the masculine image was deliberate. She was sufficiently discreet not to discuss her opinions on sexual identity and bisexuality but it came as no surprise to learn later through her writings that she was an active feminist and an avowed lesbian.

Doctor Wolff, we were to discover, was a Berlin graduate in philosophy and medicine. As a Jewess she had suffered the sickeningly familiar persecution at the hands of the Nazis and, after privations of an unbelievable order, she had been rescued and brought to England in 1936. She had been given a supernumerary appointment as a research worker at Caterham.

From very early on in her career she had devoted her attention to the study of the hand as a method of interpreting character and personality make-up. At the time we met she was engaged in a statistical survey of the main characteristics in form and dermatoglyphs of the hands of mental defectives in general. In the course of her research she had observed stigmata in the hands of mongolian imbeciles which had not hitherto been mentioned in the literature. Thus, an interest in the mongol was common to us both. Not surprisingly perhaps, she expressed keen interest in what I was doing and asked if we could collaborate in a research project which might lend support to my thesis that even the mentally subnormal, mongols included, have identifiable personalities. I was flattered and readily agreed.

She proved to be a great charmer and a most pleasant colleague to work with. Communication was a problem: she spoke broken English with a thick guttural accent, whereas I spoke "gebrochenes Deutsch" with a heaven-knows-what accent. But we got along splendidly and somehow completed what we had set out to do.

Our findings did seem to bear out my thesis. Dr Earl was impressed and encouraged us to write them up as a joint paper. For obvious reasons the actual writing fell to me, a job which I did with infinite care. The paper[2] was submitted to the *Journal of Mental Science*, the forerunner of the present *British Journal of Psychiatry*. After an agonising wait came a note of acceptance from the editor, Dr G W T H Fleming. My joy was unconfined. Although parenthood was shared, my feeling of elation at the birth of my first-born brainchild was only to be surpassed when I witnessed the birth of my first-born child many years later. Important as the paper was to me as a morale-booster, it was of equal importance to Dr Wolff in that it increased her credibility considerably.

I lost touch with Dr Wolff when I left Caterham in 1941, but I learnt that she had subsequently worked with Julian Huxley at the London Zoo in the study of palm prints of chimpanzees – a far cry indeed from the study of the hands she was to make of such glitterati as T S Eliot, Virginia Woolf, Michael Redgrave, the Duchess of Windsor, Edith Wharton, and Paul Valery. She died in London on 12 September 1986, at the age of 88. It was a privilege to have known her, to have worked with her, and to have been able to further her career in England, albeit minimally.


## THE MAUDSLEY

My new-found enthusiasm for my work was considerably heightened by the stimulus I received from attending a mandatory day-release course for a year at the Maudsley Hospital, Denmark Hill, then the flagship of the LCC Mental Health Service. In the late 1930s the Maudsley as a centre for psychiatric postgraduate teaching was at its zenith. The academic staff was as star-studded as the cast list of the National Theatre. Such excellence was due in no small measure to the intellectual windfall that had come its way as a result of the Nazi holocaust. Among those who had found sanctuary at the Maudsley were Alfred Meyer, Willi Mayer-Gross, and Erich Guttmann. All these great men were my teachers, together with such home-grown worthies as, for example, Frederic Lucien Golla, C P Blacker, and the twin brothers Eliot and Patrick Slater, not forgetting the redoubtable (Sir) Aubrey Lewis – that is, if the concept of "home-grown" can be extended to the Antipodes.

The inordinately high standard of psychiatric teaching was matched by that available in neurology. Dr Sam Nevin, a shy, self-effacing Ulsterman, was our official tutor at Maida Vale Hospital, although we were encouraged to attend the National Hospital, Queen Square. Queen Square boasted a galaxy of brilliant teachers – C P Symonds, J Purdon-Martin, McDonald Critchley, E A Carmichael, F M R Walshe, and Dennis Brinton, for example. So excellent and enjoyable were the lectures and outpatient clinical demonstrations at Queen Square that I chose to attend one or the other rather than a matinée. These, despite the troubled times, were available at many London theatres at very reasonable prices.

An added excitement of the time was to be found in the fascinating developments in research into the electrophysiology of the brain. The first substantial account of the rhythmic electrical impulses emanating from different areas of the living brain had been given by Hans Berger, a German physiologist, in 1929, to which the term Berger Rhythm had been given. These claims were treated with considerable scepticism in England until Professor Adrian at Cambridge had demonstrated beyond reasonable doubt that Berger's basic observations were correct. Professor Golla and Dr Grey Walter, a pupil of Adrian's, who hitherto had shared the scepticism, were now convinced. They began a series of investigations at the Maudsley into the brain waves in epilepsy and cerebral tumours. Their seminal papers on what was to become known as the electroencephalogram (EEG) are now classical in the literature.

I well remember the early EEG apparatus evolved by Grey Walter, a distinctly Heath Robinson contraption in which the skull electrodes were held in place by a ladies' hairnet.

There was a practical spin-off from the intense interest in electrophysiology. You did not need to be one, let alone all three, of Macbeth's witches, to foretell that a question, or questions, on the EEG would come up in the forthcoming DPM examinations, the academic end-point of my year's concentrated study. It did; three times: in the physiology, psychiatry, and neurology papers. I passed, although not to have done so after the superlative tuition I had received would have been careless, if not positively indecent.

The acquisition of the DPM in December 1939 meant that one of the two prerequisites for retention in the LCC service had been met, leaving the one about being shown to be "entirely suitable for consideration in due course for promotion" still hanging threateningly over my head. As I will explain anon, it was due to the direct intervention of Herr Hitler in my personal affairs that no medical superintendent was ever obliged to testify one way or the other.

1 Rollin H R. Personality in mongolism with special reference to the incidence of catatonic psychosis. *Amer J Mental Deficiency* 1946; **51**: 219–35.
2 Wolff C, Rollin H R. The hands of mongolian imbeciles in relation to their three personality groups. *J Mental Science* 1942; **78**: 415–18.

# 3 The Royal Air Force

In some ways the declaration of war came as a relief. The tension was becoming unbearable: it was evident to the meanest intellect that Hitler, in pursuit of his megalomanic dream of world domination, could not be stopped except by force of arms. It was evident too that in diplomatic terms Hitler would not play the game, if indeed he knew or cared what the rules of the game were. To believe otherwise was naïve. Yet Neville Chamberlain exhibited such naïveté in his lickspittle trips to the Führer in an attempt to stave off the inevitable. In all history there can be no greater insult to the wit or credulity of man than his "Peace in our time" declaration when he returned from Munich in 1938, to be followed by that monumentally inept quotation, "Out of this nettle, danger, we pluck this flower, safety."

The actual declaration was made on Sunday 3 September 1939, but there could have been no more appropriate setting for the drama than the curtain-raiser which immediately preceded it. That night there was an electric storm the like of which I have never seen before or since. Lightning, which seemed to be sustained indefinitely, turned night into day. What strangely enough heightened the awe-inspiring show of pyrotechnics was the virtual lack of thunder. Lines spoken by Lady Macbeth describe the portents of that night with uncanny perfection:

> And prophesying, with accents terrible,
> Of dire combustion and confus'd events
> New hatch'd to the woeful time.

On that fateful morning, quite spontaneously, the entire

medical staff, resident and non-resident, gathered in the medical officers' Mess. The atmosphere was understandably solemn, but as in all great tragedy an element of comic relief is mandatory. On this occasion it was provided by the medical superintendent, a veteran and, to give him his due, a casualty, of the first world war, who made his limping entrance in his white coat, his gas-mask at the ready, his tin hat sitting squarely on his white woolly head with the chinstrap in situ under his knobbly chin. He looked for all the world like a comedy version of the ghost in *Hamlet*. I took one look at the apparition and immediately fixed my gaze on a fleck of dust on my right toe-cap. I knew that if I caught the eye of one of my colleagues I would dissolve in a gale of unseemly giggles, to which on such occasions I have always been prone.

At 11 15 am Stuard Hibberd, the doyen of BBC radio newscasters (known then as wireless announcers), with his mellifluous voice and impeccable diction introduced the Prime Minister. Neville Chamberlain, sounding – understandably perhaps – more lugubrious than ever, proclaimed that because Germany had not replied to England's ultimatum demanding the withdrawal of her forces from Poland (and who in their right senses ever thought she would?), the two countries were at war. There followed an awkward silence to be broken as though on cue by the banshee wail of the air-raid siren. The war was on. The medical superintendent immediately rose and silently, and with what he hoped was quiet dignity, limped out of the room. The rest of us, not knowing what to do, did nothing. Then someone suggested it might be appropriate to break into the iron rations of Glenfiddich which we had laid down and toast the future – whatever that might be.

On Monday 4 September I was actually called up by telegram for service in the RAMC (I had been medically examined at Millbank the previous Friday, and found A1 fit). There followed an example of the ultimate in anticlimaxes: while I was actually packing my bags to go to war a motorcycle despatch rider tore up the drive of the hospital bearing a signal. My call-up was cancelled. There had been what would these days be crudely described as a bureaucratic cock-up. The right hand, unbeknown to the left, had decided that, because of the fear of an immediate assault on London by the Luftwaffe resulting in massive civilian casualties, all doctors in and around the capital were "frozen" and required to stay at their posts.

And at my post I stayed during the restless calm of the "phoney" war, the Sitzkrieg. In 1940 came the shattering defeat of the Allied forces on the mainland of Europe by the vastly superior Wehrmacht, and the subsequent miracle of Dunkirk when, against all the odds, the survivors of the British Expeditionary Force were evacuated. They did not escape unharmed: their number included hundreds of psychiatric casualties who were brought back through south-east England. Sutton Emergency Hospital (later renamed Belmont Hospital), located a few miles from Caterham, which had been set up in anticipation of such an emergency, served as the acute casualty reception station.

Belmont was singularly fortunate in having on its staff men who were not only eminent psychiatrists but who were also first class physicians, men such as Louis Minski, Eliot Slater, William Sargant, and H J Shorvon. They adopted a more all-round therapeutic approach to the acute battle neuroses which, although not excluding psychotherapy, laid emphasis on sedation, sleep treatment, modified insulin, and, in particular, barbiturate abreaction. The importance of the techniques worked out at Belmont cannot be overestimated. They were widely employed by psychiatrists in the armed forces, and later, by those dealing with civilian casualties and it is fair to say that they, in all probability, accounted for the marked reduction in chronic neurotic illnesses in the second world as compared with the first. I visited Belmont on several occasions and what I learnt there was to stand me in good stead both during my RAF service and after my return to "civvy street".

The Sitzkrieg was to be followed by the terror of the Blitzkrieg and our baptism of fire. Caterham Hospital, it should be explained, was gloriously located high on the Surrey Downs, surrounded by undulating woodlands and farmland. Strategically it was less blessed: its grounds were separated by a low fence from the Guards' depot, Caterham, and a mere 1000 yards as the Messerschmitt flew from RAF Kenley, one of a ring of fighter stations designed to defend London from the Luftwaffe. Both the depot and RAF Kenley were legitimate enemy targets so that any slight inaccuracy in the bombing meant that, even inadvertently, the hospital became the target-for-tonight.

For sleepless night after sleepless night from early August 1940 for almost three months the bombing of London and environs continued. At sundown, almost automatically, the melancholy wail of the siren sounded, to be relieved by the All Clear at dawn. The Germans were, if nothing else, regular in their habits.

The devastation was enormous: the East End of London was transformed into a sea of flame, the glow from which could be seen clearly in the night sky from Caterham, 20 miles or so away. London became a city of troglodytes, and although we ourselves didn't exactly go underground, it was felt expedient for those who, like myself, had rooms on the top deck of the hospital to move our beds down to the ground floor.

Added to these stresses was the anxiety for one's nearest and dearest. My parents and my oldest sister, Ethel, had moved out of north London to Elstree. My younger sister, Rose, a teacher, had been evacuated to Goring-on-Thames, and my youngest sister, Sonia, then a medical student, had moved with her medical school, the Royal Free, to Exeter, the inexcusable target of one of the Luftwaffe's "Baedeker" raids during which she was bombed out of her lodgings. Travel by public transport, if available at all, was hazardous. Communication by post or by telephone was difficult, and at times, impossible. There was no option but to sit and wait.

All in all it was a terrifying experience; but there were lessons to be learnt. I had only to look into myself to read the symptoms of prolonged stress, a salutary lesson which made me infinitely more sympathetic when, later on, it was my job to deal with the effects in aircrew of stress incomparably more severe than anything I had undergone.

Being in the battle area that glorious summer of 1940

brought with it some small compensation: from our elevated vantage point we had a ringside seat at the dog-fights between the fighter planes of the Luftwaffe and the RAF. So immediate was the action that it would have been foolhardy for anyone watching out of doors not to wear a tin hat as protection against the spent cartridge cases that rained down from a cloudless sky. Not infrequently we bore witness to the sickening sight of a stricken plane plunging to earth emitting as it fell an unmistakable whine followed by the final cataclysmic thud. We looked – sometimes in vain – for a parachute, which first appeared among the tangled vapour trails as a tiny white blob no bigger than a child's balloon, indicating that at least the pilot had been sufficiently alive to bale out. How alive we sometimes learnt at first hand if the hero was admitted to one of our own EMS beds, although, of course, the likes of me would not have been responsible for his treatment.

My research project completed and my thesis safely despatched to and received in Leeds, I found the routine work in the hospital tedious, unfulfillng, and frankly irrelevant. I wrote repeatedly to the appropriate committee of the BMA protesting that I was underemployed and that I might be of more value to the war effort by being allowed to join HM Forces. My offers were rejected. But then, in 1941, the deteriorating military situation dictated a change in policy and selected doctors in and around London were "unfrozen" to meet the new needs. I assume that because of my repeated applications I was the first at my hospital to be so selected. Which service, all things being equal, would I prefer?, I was asked in the official communication. Unhesitatingly, I chose the RAF. I was duly interviewed by a trio of bemedalled, heavily braided officers at the Air Ministry who showed particular interest in the fact that I was (or had been) a boxing "blue".

"Lightweight, eh? You've put on a pound or two since your student days, haven't you?" one of them asked with an inscrutable look on his face.

"Fourteen, to be exact, sir," I replied, risking a wry smile. He smiled in return.

"You'd better leave a little room for expansion in your tunic, then, hadn't you?"

I knew I was in.

* * *

I was commissioned in the RAFVR as a flying officer in June 1941 and ordered to report for preliminary training, a crash course designed to convert the likes of me into officers and gentlemen, at one of Harrogate's plush hotels which had been requisitioned by the RAF for the duration. Before actually leaving Caterham Hospital I did a round of my wards. From the male nurses, many of them ex-Guardsmen, I collected handshakes and some good advice, given with many a nudge and a wink. From the ward sisters, some with tear-stained faces, I collected an extraordinary assortment of gifts. These included bars of chocolate and, hand-knitted with loving care in RAF blue, a pair of mittens, a balaclava helmet, two pullovers, and several pairs of socks, concealed in one of which I found a ten shilling note.

It seems appropriate to add a postscript to the Caterham chapter, written not by me but by "Robbie", the superintendent's ex-secretary. Later in the letter from which I have already quoted she writes: "After you left for the RAF the great man became even more peculiar and still more peculiar until the War outside the hospital seemed of little consequence compared with that inside . . . . I retired at 50 to live a different kind of life, and perhaps one a little unique. Nevertheless I can still recall with great amusement the experience of the Gilbert and Sullivan period and think how funny it was and how sad, how very, very sad." Perhaps, after all, I wasn't as paranoid as some might be driven to think.

It may sound sacrilegious, but I enjoyed my war. It was an honour – and I use that word advisedly – to belong to an élite corps, the courage and skill of whose airmen I had recently witnessed with drooling admiration. I enjoyed, too, the camaraderie and the community of purpose – and, if the truth be known, the uniform was very becoming.

My first posting after Harrogate was to No 6 Service Flying

Training School, Little Rissington, in the very heart of the Cotswolds, there beginning a continuing and ever-deepening love affair with that most gentle, beguiling, and seductively beautiful district in all England. In addition to its unique setting, RAF Little Rissington was my first, and indeed my only, experience of a peacetime Mess which compared in comfort and facilities with a five-star hotel. I was just in time to enjoy the luxury of being served by professional batmen before they were phased out to be replaced by physically more attractive but far less efficient WAAF batwomen. There was a certain hedonistic pleasure to be got from having one's "best blue" expertly laid out and one's bath drawn before dinner. Even so, for me it was the deep, deep peace of the place that captured me, a dramatic change from the wailing sirens, the earth-shattering bombs, the high level of anxiety, and the disturbed nights that, ironical as it may seem, I had left behind me as a civilian.

My boss, the senior medical officer, a Squadron Leader Jenkins, was a pleasant, easy-going man of about my own age, a "regular" who sported "wings" above the left breast pocket of his tunic, the top button of which he ostentatiously left undone. Another indication of his "regularity" was his battered peak cap, which no recently joined VR like myself would have dared to wear. This show of sartorial one-upmanship apart, we got on very well.

He was responsible for the allocation of work to his juniors. I was somewhat shaken to be told the day after my arrival that I was to be responsible that afternoon for a lecture to the "under-training" (u/t) pilots on the physiology of high alti-tude flying, a subject about which I knew precisely nothing. Before I could protest he thrust a pamphlet into my hand.

"Don't worry," he said, "it's all in here." And it was.

What he had given me was a splendid brief written by the "boffins of Farnborough" which described simply and suc-cinctly why it was so vital to use oxygen when flying at high altitudes. Apparently, it was part of the folklore of the RAF at the outbreak of war that only "cissies" used oxygen in any circumstances. It required a determined effort by all concerned with training to dispel this firmly held belief. My first attempts to deliver the lecture were somewhat faltering, for the simple reason that I managed to keep only about one line ahead of my students; but, as always, practice makes perfect and before not too long I knew the piece by heart.

For the rest, the work was pretty routine and not very demanding. After all, we were dealing with a highly selected group of men, the physical crème-de-la-crème of their generation. I spent about six months under these near-idyllic conditions; but I knew it couldn't last. Indeed, I began to have pangs of conscience about having had it so good for so long. I needn't have bothered. When it was ordained that I must be on my way I did not have to stand upon the order of my going. I went at once: I was kicked out.

It happened this way. The station hospital was being inspected by a middle-aged group captain from Group HQ. He was a regular, and a notoriously unpleasant little man for whom the outbreak of war had meant, fortunately for him, salvation from the oblivion of retirement but, unfortunately for us, promotion way beyond his level of competence. He saw fit to question my diagnosis and treatment of a particular case and ordered me to change it. I refused. I said, politely but firmly, that although I was fully prepared to accept his orders concerning administrative matters, I must reserve my right to clinical autonomy. He flew into a towering rage and swore that he would have me off the station within 24 hours. He did. For my pains I received what was tantamount to a punitive posting, which meant that for a goodly portion of that bitter winter of 1941–2 I was downgraded to the status of an itinerant locum filling in for a week here, a week there at various elementary service flying stations (EFTS) while the single-handed medical officer was ill or on leave. More often than not I had to live in billets and, as I was to learn, the range of such accommodation was enormous. I can well remember, for example, a baronial mansion where I dined off a meagre portion of Welsh rarebit elegantly served on the crested family plate by a uniformed butler; and a two-up-two-down terrace house where the pinafored landlady regularly served a sumptuous three-course "high tea" on an assortment of plates and cutlery all of which bore the hallmarks of the jumble sale.

Accommodation when available on station was in a Nissen hut, quite unsuited to the climatic conditions then prevailing. Heating in individual rooms was primitive and depended on a coal-fired iron stove, an apparatus, as I learnt to my cost, ranked high in the hierarchy of infernal machines. It was as stubborn and self-willed as the luggage trolleys at Heathrow; it went its own malevolent way despite my best endeavours to persuade it to do otherwise. Before actually getting into bed I would stoke it to overflowing so that it glowed white hot, with the result that the temperature in the room rose accordingly. At some seemingly arbitrary hour, the evil genius in control of the machine decided that it was time that it blew itself out; and out it went. The temperature dropped like a stone, resulting in teeth-chattering mornings when to shave and dress was an heroic undertaking. It was due, I suppose, to these wildly fluctuating nocturnal temperatures that I developed a persistent laryngitis. Not only was talking painful and difficult, but I had no control over the pitch of my voice. I recall with particular embarrassment the occasion when I reported to the CO of yet another EFTS to receive a very sideways look when I introduced myself in a wavering soprano voice.

My period of penal servitude was to last well into 1942, when I was sent on temporary attachment to Abbey Lodge in Regent's Park, London, which, like other prestigious blocks of flats in that affluent neck of the woods, had been requisitioned. London was anything but a haven of peace, but at least I was back near my parents and oldest sister and such friends as had been left behind in "civvy street". In some miraculous way more than a semblance of the pre-war cultural life of London continued – cinemas, theatres, concerts, all of which I sampled with relish after my period of banishment. Abbey Lodge at that time received and processed all recruits who had volunteered for aircrew. Medical officers had their part to play in the care and instruction of these young men, but as far as I was concerned personally there were two contributions which have etched themselves permanently on my memory. The first is a lecture I had to give to a packed house of cadets at the old Odeon Cinema, Swiss Cottage, on sexually transmitted diseases, a subject about which I was better schooled, albeit only marginally, than I was about the physiology of high altitude flying. The second is of conducting FFI (free from infection) examinations on serried rows of young men "starkers" below the waist in that Holy of Holies, the Long Room at Lords, as sacrilegious an act as I have ever taken part in.

It was during one of these acts of sacrilege that HRH the Duke of Kent, shortly before he was tragically killed in a flying accident on 25 August 1942, chose to inspect us. He arrived with his entourage unannounced and, as far as we were concerned, unexpected. Neither protocol nor King's Regulations deals adequately with such an emergency. The flight sergeant in charge of the sans culottes, ever on the ball, improvised and gave the command, "Parade, stand easy" – a command which, in the circumstances, seemed somewhat inappropriate and raised an ill-suppressed grin on the faces of some of the more worldly-wise rookies.

* * *

Traditionally, in the RAF, psychiatry has played a secondary role to neurology, hence the compound noun "neuropsychiatrist", which leaves no doubt as to the order of precedence. At the outbreak of war the senior regular psychiatrist was Air Commodore Hugh Burton, who held the Diploma in Psychological Medicine. It was to his august presence that I was summoned in late 1942 or early 1943. He proved an amiable and courteous man, who explained in the course of the interview that scrutiny of the qualifications of recently joined "VRs" had revealed that I could also append the letters DPM to my name, and it was felt I might be better employed in specialist work. Did I agree? I agreed. He went on to explain that the recruitment of young women into the Women's Auxiliary Air Force (WAAF) had presented problems, a major one of which was the failure of a significant number of them to complete a trade training course. An attempt must be made to reduce this wastage by a process of preselection. To this end a research project was to be set up at RAF Bridgnorth, a large WAAF depot in Shropshire. A team of psychiatrists, psychologists, WAAF officers, and airwomen trained to administer and score group intelligence tests had been assembled. Would I agree to join them? I agreed. I agreed, although the preselection of WAAF recruits was not how I had visualised my contribution to the war effort, but in the final analysis I doubt if I had much real choice. Even to have been asked was in itself a courtesy which could well have been denied me.

RAF Bridgnorth was set in yet another glorious part of England, like the Cotswolds, that I might never have come to know but for the war. It was here that I acquired my bicycle, Pegasus (Peggy for short) which was to be my faithful companion for the rest of my service. It was only when I returned to "civvy street" that she was to be ignominiously dismembered bit by bit by thieves as she lay chained in a shed at Horton Hospital, Epsom, leaving only the frame as a skeletal reminder of her former glory. Bicycles, I should explain, were virtually the only means of transport and it was on my trusty steed that alone, or in the company of one or more colleagues, I was able to explore the highways and byways of the Shropshire immortalised by A E Housman: I can personally vouch for the authenticity of his lines, corny as they may be:

> In summertime on Bredon
> The bells they sound so clear;
> In steeples far and near,
> A happy noise to hear.

From a sociological standpoint Bridgnorth, like other WAAF depots, was essentially a matriarchy: women outnumbered men by a very considerable margin. My companions of the opposite sex with very few exceptions bore little resemblance to Amazons, the fabulous race of Scythian female warriors: for the most part they were "Mädchen in Uniform", doing their very best to do what for them comes unnaturally: trespassing, that is, on hitherto masculine preserves such as saluting, drilling, marching, and, when the occasion arose, keeping a stiff upper lip. In these abnormal circumstances it was the women who were the predators so that life for the single male was not uneventful, to say the least. But, alas, such a study was not within my terms of reference. I had been given other work to do.

The failed WAAF trainees, as Air Commodore Burton had explained, did present an urgent problem. Apart from the obvious wastage of time and money in their ineffectual training, there were the added problems of low morale and indiscipline so commonly displayed by them. So much was this the case that every effort was made to keep them away from recruits on the same depot to avoid infecting them with their dissatisfaction. It could have been that this psychopathic or sociopathic behaviour was intimately concerned with their failure and was only another facet of the general psychiatric problem.

From the point of view of preselection it was important to detect, and where possible, to eliminate from the service, or from specific trades, the unstable as well as the mentally dull. The system of preselection being used was based on the so-called GVK test devised by Dr W Stephenson, a psychologist at Oxford. The test was divided in accordance with Spearman's approach to intelligence into G (general analytical intelligence), V (verbal intelligence), and K (practical mindedness). The paper-and-pencil tests were administered by specially trained WAAF officers and airwomen. The raw scores were converted into percentiles expressing in percentage terms the standing of a particular recruit in relation to other recruits.

In theory it was hoped that anomalies in the GVK scores might act as a pointer to neurotic instability, but this proved not to be the case. However, not surprisingly perhaps, the test did provide a reasonably accurate guide to the intellectual levels of the recruits.

As to the predisposition to neurotic instability, it was found expedient to use a modified scheme devised by Air Commodore R D Gillespie, which was in turn based on the standard psychiatric interview. It was, incidentally, Gillespie who supervised this and other research projects I undertook in the RAF.

Failure in training was found to be due to (a) mental dullness, (b) neurosis, and (c) psychopathic personality. It was shown that, in the neurotic and psychopathic group, predisposition to failure as compared with a normal group was in the proportion of 4 : 1. The conclusions of the research were published in 1944.[1]

A spin-off from this major project was prompted by the casual remark of a very perceptive WAAF officer. She observed that it was the "dim" recruits who appeared to her to be more prone to parasitic infestation, particularly pediculosis capitis, or "nits", the more homely name she gave to this condition. It occurred to me that this hypothesis could easily be tested using our existing resources. The results could be of more than academic importance in that recruits found to be intellectually dull as well as infested with scabies, pediculosis, or both, might be deemed less likely to become efficient airwomen and, therefore, rejected.

The investigation was simplicity itself. Over 300 recruits who had been treated for pediculosis capitis were given the Stephenson GVK test. The scores after conversion into percentiles were compared with the percentile scores of the same number of unselected recruits who were uninfested. There was a marked difference in the scores of the two groups, the lowest scores in the three GVK tests being found in the infested group. QED! The results were published in the *BMJ*[2] in a paper dubbed by a waggish friend, "Wits and nits".

The research into WAAF trade training failures came to an end and the recommendations were implemented. From then on I was posted to various RAF hospitals or establishments which boasted psychiatric units. The chronology escapes me, but I remember Innsworth Lane, near Gloucester, in particular. Again, like most RAF stations in the UK, it was gloriously located and, as far as I was concerned, in terra incognita. So, mounted on my trusty steed, Peggy, either alone, or in the company of other officers making up the "Innsworth Wheelers", I was able to explore the surrounding countryside. I favoured the ride to Tewkesbury, not only because it was the only run on the flat, but because it brought with it the reward of sitting in the gentle peace of the abbey to listen to its magnificent organ being played in performance or in rehearsal. Other stations that come to mind are Wilmslow in Cheshire, Melksham in Wiltshire, and, much later, Cosford in the West Midlands, where the physical and psychological wrecks who had survived the Japanese POW camps were sorted out and the first steps taken towards their rehabilitation.

My memories of the various stations have fused so that I am unable to differentiate one from the other with any great clarity. Graham Greene said somewhere, "Unhappiness wonderfully aids the memory." This has not been my personal experience. Frightening or terrifying episodes have certainly produced for me indelible memories; but, for the most part, the periods when I have been most happy are also those that I can remember best. So it is that the chapters I can recall most clearly in my RAF service seem to be written against a background of high summer which, taking into account the vagaries of the English weather, must relate more to my prevailing mood than to the prevailing climatic conditions. Or were they associated with the deep and lasting friendships I made, as with Bryn and Nan Thomas and Terry Spens at Bridgnorth; Derry and Sally McQuaide at Innsworth; Arthur and Eileen Harris at Wilmslow; and Jimmie Craig in London?

\* \* \*

The last three years or so of my service were spent, apart from short periods of detachment, at the Central Medical Establishment (CME), the headquarters of the RAF medical service, in Kelvin House, Cleveland Street, W1, opposite the Middlesex Hospital. On posting I was promoted to the rank of squadron leader and, in the fullness of time, to that of wing commander. In my ascent up the ladder I learnt to shoulder responsibility and to command rather than be commanded – a lesson of far from inconsequential importance.

Central Medical Establishment was a plum posting from a professional standpoint. There, cheek by jowl, I worked with the top brass of the RAF medical branch, with men, that is, who in "civvy street" bore hallowed names now prefixed for the duration of the war by exalted ranks. (Sir) Geoffrey

Keynes, austere, remote, taciturn, was head of surgery. (Sir) John Conybeare, a gregarious, ebullient bon viveur, was boss physician. He was fond of the company of younger men and, not infrequently, I was invited to lunch or dine with him in a restaurant in the Charlotte Street area, rather more up-market than I was wont to frequent. (Sir) Geoffrey Bateman was the senior "VR" ENT surgeon and Keith Lyle senior ophthalmologist. He it was who gave his name to a physical sign reputed to be pathognomonic of Lack of Moral Fibre (LMF) – that is, the man who wore his sunglasses in the Mess. (The other comparable physical sign, attributed to Dennis Brinton, was the man whose moustaches were visible from behind.)

Not surprisingly, the men I came to know best were those with whom I worked most closely. Charles Symonds, by then Air Vice Marshal Sir Charles Symonds, whose clinical demonstrations I had attended at Queen Square, was the senior neurologist. However, as I was soon to learn, he could lay claim to more than a modicum of psychiatric expertise in that he had worked with Adolf Meyer when Johns Hopkins was in its heyday. To begin with, because I was overawed by him, I felt ill at ease in his presence, but as I got to know him better I found him to be the most approachable and delightful of men. Like so many men of real quality, he could always find time to exchange viewpoints and to offer guidance to his juniors. He remained ever-loyal to his protégés and until his death he would write me brief notes commenting on a paper or a letter I had published in the medical press. A little lower down in the neurological hierarchy were Dennis Williams, who was able, inter alia, to continue his research into the EEG, Dennis Brinton and N S (Barney) Alcock, who all together constituted a pretty formidable team.

Robert D Gillespie, physician in psychological medicine at Guy's and co-author with Professor Sir David Henderson of what was then the standard textbook of psychiatry, headed the psychiatric limb of the joint specialty with the rank of air commodore. His "regular" sidekick at CME was the popular and ever-cheerful Group Captain Victor Tompkins, who had been two or three years senior to me at Leeds. Both gave me a warm welcome to the team.

Gillespie was a tall, gaunt, scholarly man who bore a distinct resemblance to his fellow Scot, the actor Alistair Sim. Military uniform somehow ill became him and I had reason to believe that he was not entirely happy in the role in which Hitler's war had cast him. Despite his somewhat lugubrious expression he had a keen sense of humour. He was fond of telling this story, mainly because he himself appreciated its essential incongruity: In the early days of the war he had been sent to Canada together with other RAF officers on some mission, the nature of which he did not disclose. A newspaper account of the visit commented: "among the team of RAF experts to visit these shores was Wing Commander Gillespie with an unknown number of enemy aircraft to his credit."

He continued to be as helpful to me as he had been in the days of the WAAF research project and it was a matter of sorrow for me to witness the steady deterioration in his physical and mental health. A bottle of milk and a beaker were always to be seen on his desk, part of the treatment, apparently, of his peptic ulcer. But it was his deepening depression that was most distressing; and it was no surprise to me to learn of his tragic death in 1945. I attended his memorial service at Guy's Hospital chapel on 8 November 1945.

Clinically, the work of the psychiatric team at CME was mainly concerned with the assessment of the degree of disability and the disposal of members of aircrew who had developed psychoneurotic symptoms as a result of exposure to stress, mainly of a psychological nature. Stress included that arising from long-continued tension, terrifying experiences, and the depression or mourning occasioned by the loss of comrades. Loss of sleep to a greater or lesser degree was a common factor. The recommended disposal could be invaliding from the service, medical downgrading, or remustering to non-flying duties – any one of which meant loss of status and a loss of self-esteem.

The symptoms, noted subjectively by the airmen themselves or objectively by their superior officers or colleagues, included loss of initiative and confidence, irritability, cantankerousness, quarrelsomeness, and a feeling of hopelessness. Interference with normal sleep patterns was universal and included sleeplessness and terrifying dreams of air battle experiences. In many cases there was no respite from these haunting experiences even during the daytime: memories would come flooding back at any time, seemingly without conscious stimulus.

What emerged from investigation of the psychological background of these casualties was that those most predisposed to neurotic illness were the most vulnerable, and that there was an inverse ratio between the degree of predisposition and the degree of stress. What also emerged was that no person is immune and that given enough stress anyone may break down. It was of particular interest to me to note that the same equation had emerged from my work on the failure of WAAF trainees as it had with the breakdown of airmen, although it would be invidious to compare the degree of stress in absolute terms one with the other.

My debt to the RAF is incalculable, particularly so from a professional standpoint. It would have been impossible otherwise to have acquired anything like the same experience in and understanding of psychological stress in all its protean manifestations. This was an experience which was to prove invaluable when I helped to man, and in many cases found, outpatient psychiatric clinics on my return to civilian life.

* * *

There was no Mess at CME and officers posted there were required to find their own accommodation. This presented no problem. In those days highly desirable furnished accommodation was on offer at ludicrously low rentals. It was my very good fortune on arrival at CME to meet James (Jimmie) Donaldson Craig, a physician, who was also newly arrived and looking for somewhere to live. We joined forces and from a vast selection chose a furnished flat in Chelsea. I squirm to think how it would be described by estate agents today when the inclusion of a dustbin merits the appellation "luxury". Perhaps "luxurious" would be more appropriate, for such it was – and all for three guineas a week. The rightful owner, a Swiss businessman who had fled London at the outbreak of war, decided in about July 1944 that it was relatively safe to return and, understandably, wanted his flat back. An alternative home was easy to come by, this time in the shape of what could be described as – and indeed was – a bijou mews house near Regent's Park, a 10-minute leisurely stroll from Cleveland Street.

Jimmie Craig, with whom I shared both abodes, proved to be another boon companion and an ideal flat-mate. We had a number of interests in common, such as music, literature, and the theatre; but in many ways we were quite different, although our differences fortunately tended to be complementary. He, for example, was essentially untidy, whereas I tend to be the very opposite. It fell to my lot, therefore, to function as a sort of house parlourmaid. Jimmie, on the other hand, was a splendid cook and could always be relied on to produce a more than adequate meal. In this he was helped by the judicious use of items of food that were "off-ration", such as quails' eggs and haggis, with which, as a good Scot, he was very familiar and for which I acquired a lasting liking. Our larder, I must confess, was further augmented by a few under-the-counter extras provided by a good lady, appropriately named Mrs Fiddler, who served at the local branch of a grocery chain and whose penchant for RAF officers she did little to disguise.

* * *

It was Jimmie Craig who was responsible for my introduction and election to the 63 Club, a peculiarly English body, which had the flavour in a way of the coffee-houses of the seventeenth and eighteenth centuries, where friends met for literary discussion and mutual entertainment. This particular club had its origins in the Oxford of the period immediately after the first world war, in which the founder members had fought. Membership was limited to 35, 15 of whom had to be graduates of Oxford, 15 from Cambridge and five from other universities. Meetings were held once a month in London in one of the university clubs after dinner (coffee and mulled claret were served) when a member would read a paper which was afterwards discussed by other members and their guests. The membership represented a very wide spread of interests. The arts, at the time I was a member, were represented by men of the calibre of Charles Morgan, James Laver, L P Hartley and J S Collis; the law by Lord Justice Pearson; and medicine by Lord (Russell) Brain, Eric Strauss, Michael Fordham, and (Sir) Christopher Booth. There were representatives, too, from those who had made their mark in the world of education, in industry, and in public organisations, men such as (Sir) Alec Valentine, the chief executive of the old London Passenger Transport Board, who had acted as secretary of the club for as long as anyone could remember.

All in all this was a pretty awe-inspiring galère and I was never made more aware of this than when I read my first paper to the club. I had chosen Byron, my favourite anti-hero, as my subject and for weeks I beavered away refining draft after draft. Whatever merits the paper may have had were overshadowed by one painfully obvious demerit – it was too short. In my anxiety to exclude irrelevant material I had overdone the refining and as a result I ground to an embarrassing halt 10 to 15 minutes short of the time customarily allowed. It was an inauspicious début, but Eric Strauss in his kindly way attempted to minimise my discomfiture by leaping in and declaiming that so important were the issues raised in my paper that the extra time provided for discussion would be more than welcome. It was a bold, if transparent, stratagem; but it worked. The rest of the evening passed off reasonably successfully.

I remember, too, during my year as president, the anxiety that plagued me at each meeting when, by tradition, I had to introduce each speaker and open the discussion. It was the custom, too, for the president to find the guest speaker for the year. I had invited James Agate, but any arrangement with him was always attended by some anxiety. How would he behave? How would he perform? I needn't have worried; he was too good and too old a pro to give a bad performance, although on this occasion he did seem to require a disproportionate amount of whisky, then in short supply, to keep the machine well oiled.

It was impossible to be in the company of men affording so much intellectual cross-fertilisation of the highest degree not to be richly entertained and stimulated by the experience. But more important were the lessons to be learnt in the valuable art of conversation, lessons for which, in the light of my innate shyness and reticence, I shall always be grateful.

*  *  *

Living in London, in effect as a civilian, and working office hours, meant that my close identification with the RAF ceased. It was, therefore, in this hybrid state that I shared with Londoners the fluctuating fortunes of war during those fateful years 1943 to 1945.

On 13 June 1944 the first flying bomb (V1), or "doodlebug" as they were nicknamed, fell on London. Then on 8 September 1944 the first rocket bomb (V2), a true ballistic missile, ripped without any warning through the evening dusk. These were both fiendish engines of war. The Germans had virtually broken off their bombing campaign of mainland Britain in May 1941 so that Londoners had enjoyed a fairly long respite from the ravages of the Luftwaffe. The advent of the V1 and V2 was a grim reminder that Hitler, with the very able assistance of his rocketeers, Wernher von Braun and Ernst Steinhoff, still had some very nasty tricks up his sleeve.

The V1s and V2s caused a fair amount of physical damage of a local sort, but what was so psychologically devastating about them was the continuing tension they evoked: they were unpredictable, indiscriminate and, as far as the V2s were concerned, there was absolutely no defence against them once they had been launched. Conversation among civilians in the pubs and clubs at the time reflected their deepening anxiety, and I have not the slightest doubt that, as a "morale buster", Hitler was on to a winner. The increasingly grave situation was saved and, in my opinion, just in time, by the successful Allied landings on the continent of Europe, the first of which preceded the first "doodlebug" by exactly one week.

Few would doubt that D Day, 6 June 1944, was the most critical day of the war. What was so remarkable was that the preparations for this, the most ambitious and complex military operation ever mounted, were kept so secret. Certainly I, walking the corridors of power (or so I thought), had not the slightest inkling of what was going on. On the day of the initial landings on the Normandy coast, and subsequent days, we lived with our ears glued to the "wireless" in a state of suspended animation. It proved to be a triumph of unparalleled proportions. In less than a year, the impregnable fortress into which Hitler thought he had translated Europe crumbled. Victory in Europe was not so much a matter of if, but when.

\* \* \*

VE Day, when it came, was something of an anticlimax. All day on Monday 7 May 1945 we waited for the official announcement. But there was muddle and delay. Perhaps there was trouble in the celestial stage management department. Surely, anything so momentous as the declaration of peace deserved the same special effects as the declaration of war. And so eventually it came to pass: on the night of 7–8 May there was another electrical storm, this time, however, accompanied by thunder and rain in torrents, both of which elements had been conspicuously absent from the pyrotechnics which had accompanied the drama of 3–4 September, 1939.

Tuesday 8 May was to be the day. Winston Churchill was to broadcast at 3 pm and the King at 9 pm. Dutifully Jimmie Craig and I turned up at the usual time at Kelvin House; but work was unthinkable. About lunchtime we decided to damn the consequences and go AWOL. Living and working in the West End for as long as we had meant that we had come to know, and to be known in, a variety of restaurants and pubs in the locality. We had no definite plans, but decided to make our way in the direction of Buckingham Palace which, in the nature of things, was bound to be the focal point of the celebrations. We ambled down Charlotte Street and across Oxford Street, downing a celebratory one or two en route in one or two old haunts. Then the automatic pilot took over and, lo and behold, we found ourselves in our favourite lunchtime pub just off Shaftesbury Avenue. Crowds were beginning to gather, but movement was still possible.

Eventually – how much later I have no idea – we emerged into bright sunshine, turned right into Shaftesbury Avenue, and headed west into Piccadilly and beyond. The atmosphere was like nothing I have experienced before or since. The emotional lid was off: London with total abandon let down her hair, lifted her bedraggled skirts, and danced a fandango in the streets – quite literally where space permitted.

As we progressed – a soft-shoe shuffle is a more appropriate description – the crowds thickened, but we eventually made it and even found standing room on the steps of the Victoria Memorial (I could identify myself in a picture published in the press the following morning).

The scene was unbelievable and indescribable, but not, unfortunately, unforgettable. I say not unforgettable because, truth to tell, I have forgotten a good deal: and for this impairment of memory I blame the demon drink with a splash of Anno Domini. There are residual islets of memory, however, although I cannot guarantee their chronology. I remember, for example, the deafening roar which greeted the Royal Family when they appeared on the balcony, and the even greater roar when Churchill joined them there. I remember, some time later, lights being switched on in their thousands, illuminating the public buildings and monuments of London. Nelson's Column, Admiralty Arch, the National Gallery, and the Palace itself glowed rose red in the new-found light: they can never have looked more beautiful. There were fireworks galore, and to the north, in the direction of Hampstead, the night sky was alight with flickering bonfires. Searchlights swept overhead seemingly at random before miraculously coming together to form a giant cone. Torches flared in the sconces outside the clubs of St James's and Pall Mall. London, after six years of stygian darkness, was luxuriating in an orgy of light.

How, or even if, I got home that night is uncertain. Jimmie Craig, from whom I had become separated in the mêlée, was equally uncertain about his movements and no doubt for the same disreputable reasons. What I do know is that in the course of whatever went on, and wherever it happened, I lost my forage cap, headwear which in RAF parlance enjoys a cruder name. Be this as it may, the events of that incredible day are recorded, albeit negatively, by virtue of the absence of the aforementioned cap from my uniform, which our local clothes museum seemed delighted to have when, a few years ago, I had a clear out of inessential jumble.

1 Rollin H R. Trade training failures in the WAAF. Factors in predisposition and precipitation. *Br J Med Psychol* 1944; 20: 163–76.
2 Rollin H R. Pediculosis capitis and intelligence in WAAF recruits. *Br Med J* 1943; i: 475.

# 4 Return to civvy street

In 1947 I returned to the service of the London County Council Mental Health Service as a "second" medical officer, a considerable step down from the rank I had enjoyed in the RAF. Seemingly my war service proved sufficient to satisfy the second of the two prerequisites considered essential for promotion – that is, the report to be submitted by the medical superintendent as to my entire suitability for such elevation. However, I had long since decided that to work with the mentally retarded (or whatever the synonym was at that time) was not my métier and, furthermore, that I would rather offer my resignation than return to Caterham, or any kindred hospital. In the event, no heroics were necessary: I was posted to Cane Hill Hospital, Coulsdon, Surrey, like Caterham beautifully located but on the other side of the same valley. I was fortunate to be allocated rooms high up in the medical officers' quarters with a commanding view of the valley looking towards Caterham.

Cane Hill was a run-of-the-mill mental hospital peculiarly famous in those days for its herd of pedigree pigs and the packs of nocturnal wild cats that stalked the grounds. Myriad yellow eyes would frighten the life out of me as I toiled up that endless drive from Coulsdon North Station on a dark winter's night. What has happened to either or both of these peculiarities I have no idea. I would wager a pound to a penny, however, that the porkers, who required an efficient team of well trained patients to look after them, have been sacrificed on the wheel of progress, the said patients, or their successors, being now engaged in "industrial therapy" which means, in all probability, packing plastic cutlery into plastic envelopes, or some equally soul-destroying job.

46

George Lilly was then the superintendent of Cane Hill and a more amiable, easy-going, yet competent administrator it would be hard to find. He, too, was a surgeon manqué: he was never happier than when called upon to carry out whatever surgery fell within his competence. After his retirement from the LCC he became one of the last commissioners of the Board of Control before it was dissolved by the 1959 Mental Health Act. It was in this capacity that I met him when he paid official visits to Horton Hospital some time later. His boyish good humour never left him: it was always a pleasure to meet him.

But it was his deputy, Alexander Walk, to whom I am, and will continue to be, deeply indebted. Walk was another of a lengthening line of teachers whose influence shaped my career. He was the archetypal Jewish scholar, basically shy and self-effacing, who lived his life in the intellectual stratosphere. There seemed to be no subject on which he could not discourse wisely and entertainingly. He was a brilliant linguist and was able to switch into any European language, including Russian, at the drop of ein Hut, un chapeau, un sombrero, or whatever. Nevertheless, it is as a medical historian, yet another facet of his scholarship, that he will be remembered. It has been said that all philosophy is a footnote to the writings of Plato. I am no philosopher and am in no position to say yea or nay. But, thanks mainly to him, I now know some medical history and would go so far as to say that nothing can ever be usefully added to Walk's erudite contributions to the history of English psychiatry in the nineteenth century. Moreover, I was able to soak up from him, as I had previously done from my father, a reverence for books, particularly antiquarian books, all of which proved an invaluable asset when, many years later, I followed in his giant footsteps and was elected honorary librarian of the Royal College of Psychiatrists. I appreciate that I have been fulsome in praise of my mentor and friend, but I could have left it to Chaucer, who paid a far more eloquent tribute to him six centuries ago:

> But al that he mighte of his freendes hente,
> On bokes and on lerninge he it spente . . .

47

Of studie took he most cure and most hede,
Noght o word spak he more than was nede,
And that was seyd in forme and reverence,
And short and quik, and ful of hy sentence.
Sonninge in moral vertu was his speche,
And gladly wolde he lerne, and gladly teche.

Perhaps inspired by Walk, or goaded by my current lowly status in the medical hierarchy, I buckled down to work and succeeded in completing what remained of the MD examination I had started prior to joining the RAF. Armed with this higher qualification I gained promotion relatively quickly.

A year to the day after I began at Cane Hill I was transferred on promotion to Horton Hospital, Epsom, as a "first" and not long afterwards moved up to physician deputy superintendent – but not for long. With the advent of the National Health Service in 1948 the old hierarchical order changed: I was graded as a consultant and such I was to remain until my retirement in 1976. Not long afterwards I was appointed emeritus consultant, the only one so far in the history of the hospital to be so honoured.

# 5 Horton Hospital, Epsom: its history

The history of Horton is important in that, inter alia, it reflects the socioeconomic history of London in the late nineteenth century. London, primarily as the result of the Industrial Revolution, had grown enormously so that the existing facilities could no longer cope with the sheer numbers of mentally disordered arising within its boundaries. It became imperative, therefore, to build a further crop of mental hospitals to augment those built in the mid-nineteenth century. The Metropolitan Asylums Board looked for suitable land within easy – but not too easy – reach of London. Epsom at the turn of the century was an exceedingly fashionable area, boasting a number of large and elegant "Derby Houses" (some of them are still extant, but are now put to rather more plebeian use) to which the aristocratic racing fraternity would translate themselves for the races. Wealth and influence not infrequently coexist, and it was known that there would be opposition to the sale of the Horton Estate, roughly a square mile in size, for the purpose of building asylums. What added more bitterness to the pill was that the hospitals were to house "pauper lunatics", a term with most undesirable social overtones. Nevertheless, in some secrecy the sale went ahead and so did the plan to build no less than five mental hospitals to accommodate approximately 10 000 patients on the Horton Estate, of which Horton, then named Horton Asylum, was the first to be opened in 1902. It was designed to accommodate 2000 patients, but such was the demand that it was quickly filled to overflowing.

The upheaval of the first world war was responsible for the transformation in 1915 of Horton Asylum into the Horton (County of London) War Hospital. The hospital was to be commanded by the medical superintendent, Dr John R Lord, who was thereupon awarded an honorary commission. Dr Lord, now Lieutenant-Colonel J R Lord, a title to which he stuck with grim resolution, was a most remarkable man who played a central role in the development of the Royal Medico-Psychological Association (to become the Royal College of Psychiatrists in 1971), of which he was president in 1926. He was an outstanding editor of the *Journal of Mental Science*, the precursor of the *British Journal of Psychiatry*, a post he held for no less than 20 years from 1911 to 1931, having previously served as assistant editor from 1900.

The considerable talents Lord had exhibited in peacetime must have been stretched to the full in the job he was now called upon to do in war. In order to prepare Horton for its new role he had had to supervise the evacuation of 2143 mental patients from Horton to sister hospitals. Some idea of the magnitude of his new job can be gleaned from the official statistics: between 1915 and 1919 inclusive, over 30 000 officers and other ranks were received in 227 convoys.

The second world war was, as far as Horton was concerned, an action replay of its role in the first. Once again the hospital evacuated patients and donned war paint, but this time it went into action from the very beginning and did not resume its primary function as a mental hospital until late 1949, a year or so after I arrived on the scene. The staff, both medical and nursing, had been largely drawn from King's College Hospital, London, and both civilian and military casualties were treated. This time round the medical superintendent and administrator was Dr W D Nicol, who at the same time was able to keep an eye on the work being done in the vitally important malaria laboratory, in which he had a keen personal interest.


## THE HORTON MALARIA LABORATORY (THE MOTT CLINIC)

The story of the Horton Malaria Laboratory, the Mott Clinic, (or the Malaria Reference Laboratory and WHO Regional

Malaria Centre for Europe, to give it its full title) is intimately linked with the history of Horton and is well worth telling. It may read like science fiction, but it is none the less a fascinating, if little-known, chapter of science fact. The prologue is staged in Vienna about 1918 with the discovery by Professor Wagner-Jauregg of the successful treatment of syphilitic general paralysis of the insane (GPI) with malaria-induced fever. Before this epoch-making discovery GPI was a killer. One statistic suffices as evidence: in 1921 no less than 10% of all patients in British mental hospitals were victims of the disease, most of them destined to die a wretched, lingering death. News of Wagner-Jauregg's breakthrough reached the ears of the Ministry of Health in England, who immediately set out to introduce the method of treatment here.

At first, life-threatening hazards were encountered, owing largely to the failure to appreciate the lethal effects of certain species of human malaria parasites as, for example, *Plasmodium falciparum*. In one hospital alone five patients died within three weeks of being given venous blood from a malaria-infected seaman recently arrived from West Africa.

It was, indeed, in the attempt to render the treatment as safe as possible that the Horton Laboratory came to be established. Colonel S P James, the first director, laid down the criteria that should be met before a strain of parasite could be considered safe for use in man. Eventually such a strain was found in a Lascar who had contracted malaria in Madagascar. On an historic day, 25 May 1925, mosquitoes infected with this strain were taken to Horton and fed on two women patients, so establishing the so-called Madagascar strain of *P vivax* – and with it the reputation of the laboratory. To begin with the prime purpose of the laboratory was to provide malaria parasites to be used in hospitals in Britain in the treatment of GPI. So well did it meet its obligations that until penicillin made the treatment obsolete the laboratory provided material for many thousands of victims of GPI, not to mention some 16 000 who were treated in Horton alone.

Malaria therapy, it was soon discovered, provided a unique opportunity to study malaria itself in the greatest detail, an opportunity that the high-calibre personnel of the laboratory were not slow to exploit. Before long a steady stream of publications began to appear in scientific journals all over the world bearing the Horton Laboratory imprint. They record an impressive list of major discoveries, but none so important as that of the pre-erythrocytic parasite in the liver in man in 1948, a stage hitherto known to occur in monkeys, but not yet proved in man.

I well remember the drama of this particular episode. Time was of the essence in that it was known that other research laboratories were hot on the trail. A volunteer, who required malarial infection by mosquito bites, had been found. He was duly infected with *P vivax*. Seven days after the first feeding by mosquitoes, Mr E J Radley-Smith FRCS removed a small section of the liver under local anaesthetic. I myself got in on the act as a surgical assistant, proving to myself and the surgeon that my right hand had not lost its cunning and that I could still hold a retractor with the best of them. At a side door nearest to the operating theatre a motorcycle despatch rider waited. His engine was kept running, and as soon as the specimen, suitably packed, was in his possession he screeched his way to London to deliver it to the School of Tropical Medicine where technicians were all set to go. I was led to believe that the presses of the *BMJ* were held up for a time in order to publish the findings immediately if they proved to be positive. They were – and they did. Whether this dramatic frill is apochryphal I know not, but certainly a short account of the discovery was published in minimal time on 20 March 1948.[1] Everyone who had played a part in the drama was cordially thanked except, I hasten to add, the despatch rider and my goodself.

Help of inestimable value to the Allied cause was contributed by the laboratory in the last world war. The outbreak of hostilities brought to an end the cooperation between Germany and Britain in testing synthetic antimalarial drugs. The early victories of the Japanese in the Far East resulted in supplies of quinine being cut off, thus exposing our troops in North Africa and Burma to the grave danger of having to cope without adequate antimalarial drugs. Extreme urgency was given to the further development of the drug mepacrine, already known to be more effective than quinine as a curative agent. It fell to the Horton Laboratory to test the drug which, because of its potential importance, necessitated conditions of maximum security. The ultimate success of the research programme is in itself a story of epic proportions.

The laboratory was singularly fortunate in its long line of distinguished directors, starting with Colonel James and ending with Professor P C C Garnham in association with Major General Sir Gordon Covell RAMC, the latter a "verray parfit gentil knight", as over the years I was to discover. However, few would doubt that the real star of the show was Mr P G Shute OBE. He had joined the laboratory as a lab boy at its inception in 1925, and then succeeded in heaving himself up by his own boot straps to the exalted position of assistant director, a job he held until its final closure in 1973. This brilliant man, a baker by trade (given a special occasion he would produce a magnificent cake baked by himself), was by an act of providence transmuted into a world class scientist. Sir Gordon Covell told me on more than one occasion that had Shute had the right sort of academic background he would certainly have been elected FRS. And yet, so modest and self-effacing was he, that it wouldn't have made the slightest difference to his demeanour if he had been.

I was present at a simple ceremony on 2 June 1975, when, before a distinguished audience, Professor Garnham unveiled a plaque in the foyer of the Mott Clinic with the simple inscription "to commemorate the contribution made in this building between 1925 and 1965 towards the relief of suffering". It is my pleasure to record that Shute (P G, as he was invariably called by his friends among whom I have the honour to include myself) together with Miss Marjorie Maryon, his devoted technical assistant for well nigh 40 years, were present to witness the final curtain.

There is a fitting epilogue. The Wellcome Museum has undertaken the safekeeping of the laboratory's memorabilia so preserving tokens of one of the heroic chapters in the history of medicine of our time.

1 Shortt H E, Garnham P C C, Covell G, Shute P G. The pre-erythrocytic stage of human malaria. Plasmodium vivax. *Br Med J* 1948; i: 547.

# 6 Horton: an example of the evolution of the modern mental hospital

At the time I joined the staff of Horton in 1948 only a handful of mental patients had been returned from the hospitals to which they had been evacuated in 1939. In effect, Horton as a psychiatric hospital was starting from scratch. This was a mixed blessing, but on the positive side it did mean that the staff were in the unique position of being able to incorporate in the hospital's development ideas which stemmed from the changing and more enlightened approach to the treatment of the mentally disordered, of which the pioneer work of Dr T P Rees at Warlingham Park Hospital, Surrey, was a shining example. In essence this was a determined move away from the prison-like state of affairs that had previously existed, which was deemed necessary in order to contain patients, almost all of whom were held under compulsory orders. This was in spite of the provisions in the Mental Treatment Act 1930, which for the first time had permitted their admission on a temporary or voluntary basis. In keeping with the new enlightenment, greater attention was paid to the clothing worn by the patients and to their physical environment. There was a swing away from the drab, ill fitting suits and dresses of yesteryear, all of which savoured of the workhouse. More imaginative colour schemes were devised in the decoration of both the wards and the corridors, a welcome relief from the erstwhile ubiquitous dark chocolates and oleaginous greens. Similarly, yesterday's too too solid furniture, built less for comfort than for durability, gave way to something lighter and more comfortable.

Accompanying this transformation in the physical environment in which the patients lived came a determined move to counter the enforced idleness which had been one of the worst, and one of the most cruel, features of Britain's mental hospitals in the Dark Ages before the second world war. However, it is as well to remember that, as always, there were exceptions to the rule. For example, as I have already indicated, there was a well trained squad of patients engaged in pedigree pig-breeding at Cane Hill, and other mental hospitals boasted comparable concerns of an agricultural sort. The extensive gardens and grounds of all mental hospitals were immaculately maintained by teams of well trained patients, usually chronic schizophrenics, who had reached a plateau in the natural history of their psychosis. Then there were the so-called shops, the tailor's, boot-maker's, book-binder's, carpenter's, and the like, run by craftsmen who received extra payment as instructors. Worthy of special mention at Horton was the bakery, run by a master baker, Mr Smallbone by name, and a team of about 14 patients. Between them they produced the best cakes and bread in the whole of Surrey, sufficient in quantity to supply the needs of the entire hospital, and the occasional loaf that Mr Smallbone surreptitiously slipped me for my own needs. All these have gone: the gardens and grounds are today travesties of their former glory, and the bread on offer is of the tasteless, cotton-wool variety produced by commercial bakers. And all in the interests of economy!

Nevertheless, the indictment in general still holds good: apart from those centres of excellence which I have detailed and which admittedly employed only a tiny fraction of the patient population, there was enforced idleness, a state of inertia which compounded the loss of morale and self-esteem which admission to hospital in itself engendered. As a counter measure, a whole range of activities (call them "therapies" if you wish) was introduced. Occupational therapy at Horton was the core activity, and to meet its ever-increasing needs redundant wards were taken over and suitably equipped. A broad choice of activities was on offer: basket-making, weav-ing, soft toy-making, pottery, domestic science, and for the men, carpentry. The "OT" department was run by qualified, enthusiastic therapists very ably headed by the redoubtable Fay Fransella, who later crystallised out into an academic yuppie with a PhD in clinical psychology.

I appreciate that the "OT" I am describing is today considered old hat. It has been largely abandoned in favour of "industrial therapy" because, it is alleged, it reproduces modern factory conditions. Nevertheless, I maintain that if the object of OT is to provide distraction from oneself then this aim is more likely to be achieved in the production of a definable and pleasing end-product such as a rug, a piece of pottery, or a basket than something no more exciting than a plastic envelope containing plastic cutlery.

All these improvements were important and made for a more civilised and humane design for living. But what was for me the real transformation was in the spirit and atmosphere that now began to pervade the hospital, a transformation which was brought about by the injection of some of the dynamic principles of the therapeutic community, a concept so ably pioneered by Dr Maxwell Jones. In the realisation of this approach, the old rigid authoritarian attitude had to be broken down, a process which, nevertheless, had to stop short of complete permissiveness. Some discipline has to be maintained, otherwise chaos results, as some over-enthusiastic disciples of Maxwell Jones discovered to their cost.

The first step in the process of reform was to "open" the wards so that patients did not live, or rot, in isolated pockets, but had access at will to the rest of the hospital and its grounds. As an extension of this objective the railings surrounding the "exercise yards" were torn down, although security demanded that a very few wards had still to be kept locked. In the interests of the same principle of greater freedom, an increasing number of patients were allowed to visit Epsom unescorted and more and more encouraged to spend weekends with their families and friends in London.

Consideration was also given to the re-creation of social relationships, bearing in mind that a patient admitted to hospital for however long or short a time no longer belongs to his own social group and the resultant feeling of ostracism can be painful. To counter this, a programme of traditional events was arranged as, for example, dances, outings, sports events, and the like. But the real innovation was the establishment of a patients' social club, the Poplar Club, a name chosen by the original committee and derived from the Lombardy poplars which line the main avenues of the grounds. What should be clearly understood is that a club of this sort was not merely a way of enlivening the hours between the cessation of work and the time to go to bed. The true purpose of the club was as a form of group activity which was designed, as are all forms of group activity, to re-create that all-important feeling of belonging, and to satisfy that fundamental need to be needed. To this end the club was largely autonomous: I was elected president, but I tried to keep what would be known today as a low profile. It was the members themselves – that is, the patients – who were responsible for the election of officers, for the arrangement of programmes and for the general organisation, not excluding the cleaning, of their club.

The club premises were adapted from a redundant ward which was ideally suited for the purpose and which had been attractively decorated and adequately furnished. As a symbol of the patients' identification with their club, the walls were hung with framed paintings and drawings, the work of the members themselves. The Poplar Club was open every evening from 5 30 pm to 10 pm and at weekends all afternoon and evening. All patients in "open" wards, that is, more than three quarters of the patient population, were eligible for membership, and in keeping with the policy elsewhere in the hospital, the sexes mixed freely.

Finally, in recounting the innovations designed to better the spirit and atmosphere of the hospital I would stress the employment on a part-time basis of specialists in painting, drawing, pottery, drama, and music. The appeal of all these creative activities is in part an emotional one, but as so much mental illness is characterised by disturbance in feeling or emotion, any technique that will produce an inner tranquility, or an inner stimulus, is obviously therapeutically desirable. The use of the creative arts in mental hospitals in those days was experimental, but I was convinced then, as I am now, that their usefulness is limited and that they can be regarded only as ancillary or catalytic agents. I make this statement quite deliberately in an attempt to counter exaggerated claims made on their behalf, both in regard to diagnosis and treatment.

At Horton the emphasis was undoubtedly on music as a therapeutic agent, and it is for this reason that I propose to devote a chapter to the subject later on. However, I take this opportunity now to acknowledge the debt to our two music therapists, Mrs Mair Brooking, who initiated the programme in the mid 1950s, to be assisted and later succeeded by Lady Forsdyke, who remained a tower of strength until both she and I retired in 1976.

# 7 The development of outpatient departments

A sad feature of the pre-war mental hospital was its isolation. It was in effect a total institution. Security was tight and the "escape" of a patient was a serious matter demanding an inquiry and the punishment of a member, or members, of staff if dereliction of duty was discovered.

Medical officers working in mental hospitals shared in this feeling of isolation. Psychiatry was regarded as the ugly sister of general medicine, and mental deficiency was her even uglier illegitimate daughter. Academically, psychiatry was virtually ignored. Leeds University had a "part time" professor, to wit, Dr Shaw Bolton who, as I have already explained, did absolutely nothing to excite my interest in psychiatry. Edinburgh had appointed Dr George Mathew Robertson to its first chair of psychiatry in 1919, but London had to wait until 1936 before appointing Dr Edward Mapother. Leeds was the first provincial university to appoint a full-time professor (Dr H V Dicks) in 1946. As a centre for postgraduate teaching, however, the Maudsley shone like a candle in a naughty world, but access to its facilities was limited for financial and geographical reasons.

From a professional standpoint the most irksome factor for psychiatrists was the separation from the mainstream of medicine. It seems outrageous, retrospectively, that medical officers in mental hospitals had no control over the selection of the patients they were called upon to treat, nor was there any opportunity to follow them up once they had been discharged into the community.

All this was to change quite dramatically in the post-war period with the rapid spread of psychiatric outpatient clinics, particularly so after the advent of the National Health Service in 1948. For example, Horton Hospital offered no outpatient service until 1948, although it is conceivable that because of its role as an EMS hospital during the war this facility may have been delayed. At the time I was appointed to Horton in 1948 Dr W D Nicol was physician superintendent, but he enjoyed the additional and rare distinction of being consultant psychiatrist at the Royal Free Hospital, located at that time in Gray's Inn Road. It was due to his good offices that I was appointed an honorary clinical assistant to the Department of Psychiatry at that hospital.

The outpatient accommodation at the Royal Free was unglamorous to say the least. It was sparsely furnished and the white-tiled walls gave it a somewhat lavatorial appearance: but I was not in the business of comfort or aesthetics. As far as I was concerned it afforded me the same contact with colleagues in other branches of medicine as I had come to assume as my right during my service in the RAF. I now felt that I had come in from the cold and had rejoined the mainstream of medicine.

As Horton built up its numbers in terms of patients and staff there was an understandable demand for outpatient clinics to be set up in the catchment areas it served, all of them in metropolitan London. I had therefore to give up the Royal Free and in 1948 devote my energies to establishing an outpatient clinic at St Stephen's Hospital, Fulham, the first ever to be available there and the first of several I was to establish. But that is another story.

St Stephen's proved an uphill struggle, mainly because there had been virtually no preparation for me to work there. I had been appointed to the staff not by competition but by diktat, and a degree of resentment on the part of my consultant colleagues was, in a way, understandable. The accommodation available to me made that at the Royal Free almost luxurious by comparison. A linen room was all that was on offer and for equipment I had to make do with a simple table and two chairs. There was no telephone: who ever heard of a telephone in a linen cupboard? My records I kept in a shoe-box which a sympathetic outpatient sister stored for me somewhere. In spite of the manifold and manifest difficulties, however, I was in the process of proving my worth when Horton's catchment area was abruptly switched; and me with it.

This time I was to dig for psychiatric gold at New End Hospital, Hampstead, and the Nelson Hospital, Wimbledon. Let it be known that of all the general hospitals I have ever served, New End is the one to which I feel most indebted not only because of the invaluable professional experience I gained there, but because, on a more personal level, it took such exemplary care of my father and mother when they, at different times, were patients there.

New End was an architectural disaster. It had been originally a workhouse hospital and had been modified time and again in a brave attempt to transform it into some semblance of a modern hospital. The attempt failed; but this did not prevent New End becoming a centre of national, if not international, repute, particularly in endocrinology. The architect of this phenomenal success was undoubtedly John (Jack) Piercy, the surgeon superintendent, who emerged as one of the world's finest thyroid surgeons. In addition, however, he was the most caring of doctors. I don't know when, or even if, he ever slept, but I do know that when my mother's life hung by a thread he spent long periods night after night at her bedside until she miraculously began to recover. Jack Piercy became a legend in his own hospital and in his own lifetime; the award of the CBE late in his life can only be regarded as a belated recognition of his services to the hospital and to the community it served.

Around him Piercy gathered a pretty formidable team of colleagues among whom were those similarly interested in endocrinology. As physicians there were, for example, Raymond Greene and A S Mason. Among the surgeons was Geoffrey Keynes, who carried out his thymectomy operations in the treatment of myasthenia gravis at the hospital. I came across Keynes quite often at New End, but I found him just as remote and aloof as I had come to know him, or, rather, not to know him, in the RAF. It was at New End, incidentally, that I first met (Sir) Raymond Hoffenberg shortly after he had shaken the dust of his native South Africa from his shoes. He was to become president of the Royal College of Physicians and simultaneously president of Wolfson College, Oxford.

Surrounded as I was by endocrinologists and their associated clinical problems, it would have been inconceivable for me not to become involved. I did; and as witness thereof I point to a meeting of the clinical section of the Royal Society of Medicine in 1953 where I presented a case of myxoedematous madness. Richard Asher, who had first described the syndrome, was present at the meeting and commented on my paper, an abstract of which was published, together with his commentary.[1]

New End provided a psychiatric clinic for all seasons. Cases were referred to it by physicians and surgeons on the staff of the hospital, and by GPs in the neighbourhood. Inpatients who had been treated at Horton were followed up, and if necessary, readmitted there. Domiciliary visits were carried out at the invitation of local GPs or mental welfare officers. The work-load increased rapidly so that it was not too long before I had to invoke the assistance of a senior registrar and a psychiatric social worker. All of us worked flat out every Wednesday morning, starting promptly at 10 am until we had eventually to surrender to the frantic appeals of the outpatient sister who had to prepare for another clinic beginning at 2 pm.

It is a revealing fact that, when I had first discussed starting the clinic at New End in 1948, it had been suggested that my attendance for an hour or two every two or three weeks might be all that was required. This anecdotal fact is an illustration of the universal failure of the lay authorities to estimate the psychiatric needs of a community. The truth is that the more facilities that are provided, the more the need is exposed, a need which is, in fact, inexhaustible. This was proved at New End and again at every other clinic I have started. Nor do I claim this discovery to be peculiar to myself.

I continued very happily at New End until mid-1974 when some bureaucrat somewhere had a sudden rush of blood to the head and decided that Horton's catchment area must change yet again and, ipso facto, my attendance at New End must cease. I was so incensed by this cavalier treatment that I wrote the following letter to the *British Medical Journal*[2] which expresses very adequately my feelings at the time:

SIR, – May I be allowed to sketch a face of our National Health Service – one oddly enough, that has nothing at all to do with money?

In 1948 I was appointed a consultant psychiatrist. I had at that time two burning enthusiasms. One was for the NHS itself; the other was to extend psychiatry into the general hospitals. But which? The deciding factor was, I learnt to my cost, the catchment area of the parent mental hospital.

In the original allocation of catchment areas, Horton Hospital, Epsom, my parent hospital, was allocated that part of the metropolis in which St Stephen's Hospital, Fulham, was located. I was instructed to start a clinic at that hospital and in 1948 I did so, gleefully and enthusiastically. Some months later we were informed that our catchment areas had been changed and that Horton was to take over, inter alia, the Hampstead area and part of Merton. Believing as I did then in the omniscience of bureaucrats and their divine right to order these things, I respectfully touched my forelock, packed up at St Stephen's and in 1949 began to plough my lonely furrow at New End Hospital, Hampstead, and the Nelson Hospital, Wimbledon. In 1960 the chaps with the maps decided that the Royal London Homoeopathic Hospital should be linked with Horton Hospital and it was suggested that I attend there on an "as required" basis. Obediently I did so, but not for long. The same chaps had had a second think and had decided that the Homoeopathic be linked with another hospital. I was asked to cease to attend.

However, the New End and Nelson clinics flourished, particularly the former, where facilities existed for expansion. Before not too long the services of two additional consultant colleagues were necessary in order to cope with the work. Together we offered a service to the hospital itself, to our colleagues in other medical disciplines, and to the general practitioners in the district. In 1970 Horton's catchment area was changed again. Virtually overnight the service that had been built up over a period of two decades at New End collapsed. There were protests from colleagues at the hospital, from the GPs, and from the patients themselves, but all to no avail.

The bureaucrats now decided in their strange, arbitrary way that Horton must take over the psychiatric needs of part of the Borough of Richmond. This time I was detailed to start up at St Mary's Hospital, Hampton. With perhaps less glee and less enthusiasm I did so. It is easy to demonstrate that there is always an untapped need for psychiatric services in any community; the clinic itself and the domiciliary service grew and I began to enjoy working with my new patients and colleagues.

It is hard to believe that one can have the ground cut from beneath one's feet for a fourth time in a single career but, lo and behold, the bureaucrats decided that it was imperative that catchment areas be realigned. The same protests from the same sources that had been made at New End were echoed, but the decision was final and at the end of September this year I ceased to attend St Mary's.

The picture I have drawn is, I think you will agree, unattractive and unacceptable. The wart which disfigures it most, in my opinion, is the assumption by the powers that be that hospitals in the NHS can be treated like shops in a multiple chain-store organisation. They seem to have forgotten, if they ever knew, that the practice of medicine, and that of psychiatry in particular, has to do with people and that it has to do with patient-doctor relationships, some of which have had to be built up over a period of years. Doctors and their patients, may I remind them, are not packets of soap-flakes that can be moved from one shelf to the next shelf or from one shop to the next shop with impunity.

Do I sound disenchanted, disillusioned, or even a trifle paranoid? I am. I bloody well am. – I am, etc,

HENRY R ROLLIN

Horton Hospital
Epsom, Surrey

1 Rollin H R. Myxoedema associated with paranoid states treated with thyroid extract. *Proc R Soc Med* 1953; **46**: 718.
2 Rollin H R. All change. *Br Med J* 1974; **ii**: 341.

# 8 The changing face of madness

It is an intriguing and, to me, inexplicable phenomenon how the face of madness has changed in my professional lifetime. In the 1930s a goodly proportion of patients in mental hospitals, or "asylums" as they were then called, still exhibited gross and/or bizarre manifestations of their illness. There were those suffering, for example, from schizophrenia, (and I use this term as Bleuler intended it to be used, as a description of a group of similar, but by no means identical, illnesses), who spent their entire day in assumed statuesque postures; others who endlessly carried out strange and seemingly meaningless rituals, or who rocked rhythmically and tirelessly backwards and forwards in their chairs. Cases of flexibilitas cerea, or waxy flexibility, whereby limbs can be moulded into strange postures which can be maintained for prolonged periods, were easy to come by. Other patients showed grossly depraved habits, such as faeces-eating or smearing, and some filled their day in open and unashamed masturbation. Where are they now?

A particular management problem was presented by schizophrenics who manifested their psychosis in disturbances of behaviour – disturbances which ranged through the entire catatonic spectrum from wild excitement at one end to stupor at the other. All these deviations from the norm were the hallmarks of the lunatics of the textbook and the lunatics of the fiction of yesteryear, deviations so gross as to alienate the victims from the community of man. These were the lunatics whose antics were so grotesque as to be considered entertainment and worth paying money to see, as did the visitors to Bethlem Hospital (Bedlam) in the seventeenth and eighteenth centuries. On the other hand, these were the same lunatics whose behaviour was at the same time so incomprehensible as to strike terror into the heart of the ordinary man. Fear, I believe, is the parent of cruelty and it is because of this fear that the demand was made for lunatics to be locked away. Hence the prison-like conditions in which they were formally incarcerated. Where are these same "lunatics" today?

Comparable, but far fewer in numbers, were those patients deemed to be suffering from the affective psychoses whose major symptoms were to be seen in gross disturbances of mood. In this group there was no shortage of victims of wild, uncontrolled psychomotor excitement who could quite literally die from what was termed "exhaustion of mania", a cause of death accepted in those days by the Registrar. At the other extreme of this affective disease were victims of psychomotor retardation in which depression reached such depths as to lead to stupor. This, too, constituted a distinct threat to life as the result of starvation: forced feeding of these unfortunates was a well practised technique which I have not only witnessed but have been party to. More importantly, there was the danger of death by suicide. The attempt to prevent suicide, or self-mutilation, was a major preoccupation. These were the days of the infamous "suicidal caution card", a document every member of staff involved in treatment was obliged to sign. Writ large in red lettering on top of the card was the injunction that the patient "must on no account be allowed out of observation, not even in the WCs." And so to the anguished, guilt-ridden, self-accusatory wretches even the privacy of the privy was denied. In spite of these elaborate precautions, depressed patients still succeeded in killing or mutilating themselves. I remember, for instance, a Cockney costermonger who drowned himself, within the grounds of the hospital, in an animal drinking trough containing just a few inches of water; and a brilliant, refugee engineer who castrated himself with a razor blade smuggled into the hospital by a visitor who had been "conned" into doing so. It would be idle to suppose that today suicide or mutilation have disappeared, but the numbers have certainly been reduced.

I said at the beginning of this chapter that the dramatic change in the face of madness was inexplicable. Even so, it is at least possible to put forward hypotheses. Is it, for example, due to an evolutionary process in the natural history of mental illness? This is singularly unlikely considering the relatively tiny timespan concerned. No: if I were to be hard pressed I would put my money on a combination of two vital factors; firstly, the overall improvement in the atmosphere in mental hospitals, and, secondly, the concomitant change in the therapeutic climate.

I have already discussed at some length the changes in the atmosphere brought about by a more relaxed regimen, and by the upgrading in the décor and the furnishings of the wards. These went hand in hand with improved clothing for the patients, a change from the drab uniform workhouse dresses and suits to brighter less uniform garments in which choice was a possibility. Above all, there was a multi-pronged attempt to counter the enforced idleness, and the subsequent loss of dignity and individuality which added to the totality of misfortunes that patients had to endure. This does not mean that there was any deliberate physical ill-treatment, or if there was I was never witness to it. What damage was done was psychological: in essence it was a gradual process of dehumanisation and desocialisation which progressively reduced the patients' chances of readapting to the needs of the greater community if and when they were discharged.

## TREATMENT: FROM NIHILISM TO CAUTIOUS OPTIMISM

To turn now to the changes in treatment, by which I mean methods aimed specifically at the eradication or amelioration of the disease process itself. About this time indications of imminent change were in the air. The Mental Treatment Act 1930 was enormously important, both symbolically and in actuality. It meant that for the first time persons suffering from mental illness could be admitted to mental hospitals on a temporary or voluntary basis, so avoiding the stigma of certification – a stigma which, like a sentence of imprisonment, would have stuck to them for the rest of their lives. By implication, therefore, hope if not charity was written into the legislation. The inclusion of the word "treatment" in the title of the Act was also an important first: never before had it appeared in the heading of any instrument of legislation to do with the mentally disordered. Perhaps psychiatry, and in turn, the legislature, had been inspired by the contemporaneous epoch-making therapeutic advances in general medicine, of which the newly discovered drug prontosil, a forerunner of the sulphonamides, is an excellent example.

It was during my gypsy period that, quite fortuitously, I worked as a locum for some months in a small well organised hospital in Leicestershire. I and a young whimsical Glaswegian, whose accent you could cut with a knife, but whose name escapes me, were the only two resident doctors. There was no pharmacist on the staff, so that what dispensing had to be done was done by us. At dinner one evening my colleague suddenly declared with all the passion of a divine revelation, to which his accent added dramatic weight, that what our patients, for the most part schizophrenics of varying degrees of chronicity, needed was "not sedation, but stimulation!" At this time in the late '30s psychiatry, by which I mean institutional psychiatry – there was little else on offer – was somnolent, if not asleep. This reduced state of consciousness was due in no small measure to the sedative drugs, the bromides and paraldehyde which were doled out to the patients by the bucketful. My colleague's declaration, although tinged with whimsy, was nevertheless extremely pertinent. Instant action was demanded. We there and then made our way to the dispensary where we concocted a mixture of so-called "tonics" in two winchesters, one full-strength and the other half-strength. The first we labelled in excruciating dog Latin, "Mist omnibus robusta", and the other, "Mist omnibus lenta". We then proceeded to reduce, or omit, the dose of bromide or paraldehyde prescribed for our schizophrenic patients and to substitute one or other of our stimulating mixtures. The results were far from dramatic, but nevertheless apparent: our patients, for the time I remained at the hospital were less somnolent, and the stench of paraldehyde was certainly less pungent. Our experiment, naïve as it certainly was, reflected the current Zeitgeist. Throughout the civilised world the same stirrings were to be felt, although other means to the same end were infinitely more heroic, but for the most part far less innocuous.

Von Meduna, who was the first of what proved to be a veritable International Brigade of workers, made his contribution in Budapest in 1934. He based his work on the premise, entirely false as it so happens, that epilepsy and the catatonic variety of schizophrenia were incompatible and could not, therefore, co-exist in the same person. He argued that, if artificial epileptiform convulsions could be induced in patients suffering from schizophrenia, the disease process – whatever that might be – would be attacked or possibly eradicated. To this end, after a series of animal experiments, convulsions were induced in patients by intramuscular injections of 25% camphor in oil. The results were variable, but the side effects – namely, delirium, prolonged vomiting, and pain at the site of the injection – were so unacceptable that this particular convulsant agent had to be abandoned. After further experiments, Von Meduna introduced leptazol (Cardiazol), a cardiac stimulant, as a safe and reliable agent.

Safe and reliable it may have been, but there was a very considerable and understandable reluctance on the part of most patients – no matter how psychotic they happened to be – to continue the treatment. This was because the pre-convulsive experience, for which no amnesia resulted, was so terrifying that repetition was to be avoided at all costs. I can well remember at the same Leicestershire hospital the unseemly and tragic farce of an unwilling patient being pursued by a posse of nurses with me, a fully charged syringe in my hand, bringing up the rear. This catch-as-catch-can method of treatment struck me as inhumane and I was at one with the nurses in refusing to go on with it. Nevertheless, in 1937 Kennedy, in a seminal paper based on the results of over 1000 selected cases so treated, maintained that there was a complete remission rate of over 70%, not including partial or "social" remissions.[1]

About this time too Sakel in Vienna, following a series of hunches, used insulin-induced hypoglycaemia in the treatment of schizophrenia. So favourable (apparently) were the reported results of this method that clinics rapidly sprang up throughout Europe and America. Again, extravagant claims were made: Pullar-Strecker in 1938, for example, claimed that, "Taking the spontaneous remission figures, we find that 23.6% of the total cases remitted, whereas practically double that number remitted with insulin treatment." He went on to make the categorical claim that "insulin therapy does constitute a decided advance in the treatment of schizophrenia."[2]

Italy joined the International Brigade in the war on schizophrenia in 1937. There was still faith in the method of artificial epileptiform convulsions, but the inhumanity of Cardiazol as an agent was now universally recognised and an alternative was sought. Cerletti and Bini first introduced electroconvulsive therapy (ECT) in 1938 as an alternative, and it was not long before papers appeared in prestigious journals claiming success rates that varied widely, but which were all decidedly encouraging. For example, in 1943 two staunch advocates of ECT, Kalinowsky and Worthing, stated in their conclusions: "The rate of remission (recovered and much improved) is 67.4% for cases of less than six months' duration, 43.1% between six months and two years' duration and 9.2% in those of more than two years' duration."[3] The least that could be claimed incidentally for ECT as compared with Cardiazol was the complete amnesia for the pre-convulsive period, in itself an enormous advance.

The saga continues with what I consider to be the most regrettable innovation in the treatment of schizophrenia, namely, the blind mutilating operation on the brain – the so-called pre-frontal leucotomy (or lobotomy), introduced by Moniz in Portugal in 1936 and first performed in Britain at the Burden Institute in Bristol in 1940. The proponents of the operation were loud in its praise. Fleming, editor of the *Journal of Mental Science* and an influential figure in British psychiatry, described pre-frontal leucotomy as "one of the most startling of modern therapeutic procedures", and sharply rebuked those who dared criticise it. "There has been some hostile criticism of the operation by medical men with no experience of it and little experience of psychiatry," Fleming thundered in his typical grand seigneurial way in the same paper.[4] At the time he was writing (May 1943), some 350 leucotomies had been performed in Great Britain and, in an analysis of 184 reported by seven authors, Fleming deduced that 72 were much improved and 44 improved.

My service in the RAF had provided little or no experience of the so-called physical methods of treatment of mental illness and it was only after I was appointed to Horton in 1948 that I was to serve my apprenticeship in the use of these methods. I was sent on secondment with a team of nurses to Belmont Hospital, Sutton, Surrey, where there was an established deep insulin therapy (DIT) clinic, to learn the procedure, which was far from simple, at times hazardous, and occasionally fatal. Suitably enlightened, we set up our own clinics at Horton, one on the male and another on the female side. Buoyed up with enthusiasm, staff morale in the DIT clinics was inordinately high. Not only were we doing real physical doctoring and nursing, but we believed absolutely in the worthwhileness of what we were doing, despite the fact that some of our patients took on a grotesque bloated appearance as a result of the inordinate amount of weight they gained.

At Belmont we were also instructed in the use of ECT, in those early days given "straight" – that is, without muscle relaxants or intravenous anaesthetics. The great danger of this primitive method arose at the onset of the fit as a result of the violent spasm of powerful extensor muscles, and it was in an attempt to offset this danger that a squad of nurses was trained to exert pressure on the shoulders, hips, and legs. Even so, dislocations and fractures of the long bones and crush fractures of the lower dorsal and lumbar vertebrae were by no means uncommon. A further hazard lay in the complexity and unreliability of the early ECT machines resulting in a "failed fit". The failure to induce a convulsion left the patient with a thumping headache, and a well deserved resentment against his doctors and nurses. Nevertheless, we were so convinced of the efficacy of the treatment, particularly in the acute phase of schizophrenia and for the "maintenance" of chronic cases, that ECT clinics were the order of the day. Clinics were held at least twice a week during which 20 to 30 cases were treated, and, all in all, they formed a major item in the therapeutic programme of the hospital.

So carried along were we by the claims made by our elders and betters that we at Horton played our part, and with enthusiasm, in the rush to recommend patients for pre-frontal leucotomy. To put the popularity of leucotomy into perspective, statistics show that by 1963 in Great Britain the number of operations reported exceeded 15 000. I confess that I was guilty of recommending the operation for 20 or so of my schizophrenic patients, and, may I add, nothing I have done weighs more heavily on my conscience. The basis for my guilt lies in the fact that not only did I not see any lasting benefit in one single case, but the sequelae of the operation in some cases were quite appalling. These included postoperative epilepsy, cerebral haemorrhage, and, probably worst of all, postoperative personality change, mainly characterised by disinhibition. I recall with particular shame a young attractive schizophrenic girl, bien élevée, and from a good Catholic family for whom permission for the operation had to be obtained from a Catholic psychiatrist. This was granted and the operation went ahead. Her physical recovery was uneventful, but during her convalescence she began to exhibit shameless, disinhibited sexual behaviour. She absconded from the hospital with a most undesirable male patient, a psychopath, who, it appears, proceeded to put her on the streets and live off her immoral earnings. When eventually the couple were discovered by the police, the girl was undernourished, her body filthy and lice-infested; but she expressed no shame and certainly no regrets whatsoever for her escapade. That her parents refused point-blank to allow her to return to Horton was fully understandable and I had, therefore, no way of knowing what happened to her. I cannot imagine, however, how further disasters could have been avoided.

The era I have just discussed was the era of Sargant and Slater, the high-noon of physical methods in psychiatric treatment.[5] They were heady days for psychiatrists, who like myself were still in the main mental hospital based. Optimism rode high, so high, in fact, that we were convinced that the psychiatric millenium was just around the corner. But rationality eventually re-established itself as we appraised, or reappraised, the results of what we had been doing. We awoke, in effect, from our wish-fulfilling dream to the realisation that what we had been unwittingly party to was a variation of the oldest morality play in the repertoire – The Emperor's New Clothes. By the mid-1950s Cardiazol had been abandoned completely and the deep insulin clinics dismantled. The flood of pre-frontal leucotomies was reduced to a trickle, and those that were performed were in special centres where infinitely more precise techniques were available. The operation was now carried out largely for conditions other than schizophrenia – for example, severe chronic depression and disabling obsessional neurosis. Electroconvulsive therapy, the sole survivor of le grand siècle, was now administered with the aid of muscle relaxants and intravenous anaesthetics given by professional anaesthetists. The patients selected for treatment were rarely schizophrenics – with the exception of those in catatonic stupor, for whom ECT could achieve dramatic and, at times, life-saving results. What ECT came to be used for, and continues to be used for, is the treatment of the affective disorders, particularly depression: and it continues to be a rule of thumb that the more profound the depression the more likely it is that it will respond.

It was fortunate for our morale, sadly punctured by the disappointment with, and reduction in, the use of physical methods of treatment, that almost contemporaneously the most important revolution in the history of treatment in psychiatry was taking place. I refer, of course, to the era of psychopharmacology. In 1952 the French firm of Rhone-Poulenc marketed a phenothiazine, chlorpromazine, as Largactil ("large activity"). Its use under various names tore through the civilised world like a whirlwind and engulfed the whole treatment spectrum of psychiatric disorders. For instance, in the USA, under the name of Thorazine it was prescribed for an estimated two million patients within eight months of its introduction there in 1954. Since then there has been a constant stream of so-called psychotropic drugs coming off the pharmaceutical production lines. And the cry is – still they come!

Despite any reservations I may have, and I have quite a few, I would be the first to concede the enormous importance of these drugs. However, their toxicity, as manifested by their side effects, needs to be constantly watched. I might mention as a footnote to the history of the introduction of psychopharmacology in the early 1950s the particularly alarming reaction in both patients and staff to Largactil, so serious as to threaten its utilisation. It was found that a considerable proportion of those to whom the drug was given and by whom it was administered – doctors, nurses and auxilliaries alike – suffered severe skin rashes which were aggravated by exposure to the sun. The reaction was so severe and intractable that it became impossible for those affected to work with patients who were being treated with the drug, to a degree that their careers in psychiatry were thrown in jeopardy. Fortunately for everyone concerned, it was found that the root cause of the hypersensitivity was an impurity in the drug and not the drug itself. The impurity was removed and all was well; but it was a closely run thing.

From a practical standpoint, the main virtue of the new drugs was that they were easy to handle and could be administered by psychiatrists in outpatients. General practitioners could be instructed in their use and, in particular, how to keep a weather eye open for side effects. If admission to mental hospital became imperative, the stay of patients there could be measured in weeks rather than months, although I soon discovered that shortness of stay may not in itself be a reliable guide to the long-term prognosis. Nevertheless, their usefulness in aborting an acute episode of schizophrenia seemed undoubted. Their efficacy, however, in chronic states of the illness – and it is estimated that one third of all cases still become chronic – is more debatable. It could well be that, in some cases doomed to become chronic, acute relapses may be prevented; but not without cost. The side effects induced by psychotropic drugs, given orally or by injection, may be pretty intolerable. It would be apropos to mention a somewhat cynical remark made not too long ago by a professor of psychiatry at a conference I attended in Wales. "With these drugs," he said, "the treatment can so easily become the disease." And one percipient and articulate patient reflected, "I think that the richness of my pre-injection days [of Moditen, a long-acting phenothiazine] – even with brief outbursts of madness – is preferable to the numbed cabbage that I have become."[6] Another patient remarked with comparable poignancy: "Medication obviously plays a part but somehow I prefer to be a little 'mad' than overdosed by major tranquillisers."[7] It is when faced with such a cri de coeur that, somewhere in the inner recesses of my mind, I hear the inspired slogan of my impish Scots colleague in Leicestershire: "Not sedation, but stimulation!" There is a danger, as I see it, that by the injudicious use (or abuse) of psychiatric or tranquillising drugs – call them what you will – we may be edging back to something akin to the era of bromides and paraldehyde from which we escaped half a century ago. Which is where I came in.

1  Kennedy A. Convulsion therapy in schizophrenia. *J Mental Science* 1937; **83**: 610–29.
2  Pullar-Strecker H. Insulin treatment of schizophrenia. Recent advances in insulin treatment. *J Mental Science* 1938; **84**: 146–55.
3  Kalinowsky L B, Worthing H J. Results with electric convulsive therapy in 200 cases of schizophrenia. *Psychiatric Quarterly* 1943; **17**: 144–53.
4  Fleming G W T H. Prefrontal leucotomy. *J Mental Science* 1944; **90**: 486–500.
5  Sargant W, Slater E. *Physical methods of treatment in psychiatry.* London: E & S Livingstone, 1963.
6  Westcott P. One man's schizophrenic illness. *Br Med J* 1979; **i**: 989–90.
7  Creer C, Wing J. *Schizophrenia at home.* Surbiton: National Schizophrenia Fellowship, 1974.

# 9 The dissolution of the mental hospital and the myth of community care

It is a curious irony that at the very time that British mental hospitals were enjoying their greatest international fame – visitors would arrive from all over the world to admire them and to learn from what had been achieved – the plans for their destruction were being laid down. Enoch Powell, then the Minister of Health, was the architect although it is only fair to say that the same policy has been rigorously pursued by subsequent ministers, no matter what their political colour.

Mr Powell in his famous, or infamous, Hospital Plan 1962, described our mental hospitals with more eloquence than accuracy as: "majestic, brooding structures, dominated by the twin ideas of isolation and custodialism, housed in depressing and decaying buildings, suffering from acute staff shortages."[1] He foresaw that by 1975 half the hospitals should have been pulled down and their functions split between psychiatric units in general hospitals and community care.

There can be no doubt that official government policy was based on papers published in 1961 by different authors forecasting that, as the result of statistical analyses of current trends, the future needs of beds in British mental hospitals would be halved. Chief among these was a paper by G C Tooth and E M Brooke, who maintained that in future there was likely to be a need for 1.8 beds per 1000 of the population instead of 3.4 per 1000 as it was then.[2] K W Gross and Janet Yates in a regional study in the Birmingham area gave much the same results as in the national survey.[3] Alan Norton in a single hospital study lent support to the conclusions of the authors of the two papers mentioned.[4]

So the passing knell of the mental hospital was sounded, and what was tantamount to a memorial service was read by

Dr W S Maclay, a former principal medical officer to the Ministry of Health, in his Barton Pope lecture given in Adelaide, Australia, in 1963.[5]

The publication of these papers and the Minister of Health's pronouncement split the psychiatric establishment in two. A state of civil – almost at times uncivil – war broke out between the proponents and opponents of "the plan". At meetings of learned societies and in the correspondence columns of medical journals men spoke or wrote with fire in their bellies. Let it be said that it was regarded as progressive to favour "the plan" and grossly reactionary, if not sacrilegious, to oppose it.

I sided not with the angels. As on a previous occasion, I felt like the small child in the fable of the Emperor's New Clothes who refused to acknowledge the existence of sartorial miracles which were not apparent to him. Similarly, I could not see the extent of the therapeutic miracles which were loudly proclaimed on all sides; nor could I see how mental hospitals with all their shortcomings had been transformed overnight from good objects into bad; nor could I see how such reliance could be placed on the concept of "community care" when no fieldwork had been done to prove that the community did care.

The reason for my scepticism was that our experience at Horton was so much at variance with alleged trends elsewhere that I decided to go to war myself and join forces with the "reactionaries". In support of the cause I fired quite a few broadsides. For example, in a letter to the *Lancet* in 1963, I pointed out that Horton far from "running down" was "running up" at an alarming rate.[6] The number of beds occupied had risen from 1449 in 1958 to 1503 in 1962. The annual number of admissions had soared from 1080 to 1753 in the same period. The increase had taken place in spite of a rise in the number of outpatient consultations in clinics held in our catchment area from 4697 to 7370. The establishment of a day hospital in Paddington had no perceptible effect on the demand for beds in the parent hospital.

Again, to go back a bit, prompted by Alan Norton's paper[4] I wrote a letter to the *British Medical Journal* in 1961[7] which was published in extenso and which I take the liberty of reproducing here:

SIR, – Whilst I congratulate my old friend and colleague, Dr Alan Norton, on his most valuable paper, "Mental Hospital Ins and Outs" he will, I know, forgive me if I venture some criticism of, and a few reflections on, his findings.

My major disquiet relates to the data on which Dr Norton strikes a more optimistic note on the prognosis in schizophrenia. His optimism, so far as I can determine, rests on twin piers: the improved response to modern methods of treatment, and the increased discharge rate from, or conversely the shorter stay in, hospital. The two are, of course, largely interdependent. Little or no mention is made by Dr Norton of the natural history of the disease as a factor in prognosis. Schizophrenia is characterised by recurrent remissions and relapses which, needless to say, can occur without any specific treatment. Each relapse wounds the total personality more deeply so that subsequent remissions are less and less complete. At some arbitrary point along the road it is justifiable to term the case "chronic," or "long term," to use a current euphemism. It is my impression that the effect of modern methods is to precipitate a remission earlier than might otherwise have been expected. But what they seemingly do not do is to prevent relapses. How else can one explain the alarming number of relapses, represented by readmissions, which must include a proportion of the sort of case whose response to treatment would have been classified as "very good". So the patients come back, are further treated with perhaps less satisfactory results, and go again. How often this cycle can be repeated depends on individual cases, but it can be frighteningly frequent. In effect, the "open-door" policy of yesterday has been transmuted into the "revolving-door" policy of today. This new policy may or may not be desirable, but it cannot fairly be used as a measure of prognosis. A disease is no less chronic because its manifestations can and do continue outside as well as inside hospital.

The discharge rate as an index of recovery, or even improvement, in mental illness bristles with fallacies. One of the ironies of the enormous and most welcome increase in voluntary (now informal) admission to mental hospitals in recent years is that patients, particularly schizophrenics, elect to leave hospital before they are well enough to do so. Not only may the patients be no better on leaving: they may in fact be worse. Their self-discharge may be an expression of the loss of insight into their illness which prompted them to seek medical help in the first instance; or it may be an act of impulsiveness such as is seen so often in schizophrenics. Furthermore, the discharge rate may be determined by the policy of an individual hospital. Paradoxically enough, a hospital which concerns itself with ensuring work and accommodation for its patients prior to discharge – and this is often difficult and time-consuming – may have a lower discharge rate than one which is less exacting in these respects.

Another major flaw, as I see it, in Dr Norton's argument is in his failure to follow-up his discharged cases. The only reference I can find to their fate after leaving hospital is in a somewhat nebulous statement – that is, "At least she is now at home and often at work for the greater part of the time." No idea is given of how many are at home, or how long they have stayed there, or how many are at work. Although ideally home is where the schizophrenic should be, all homes are not ideal. Schizophrenics tend to have strange, if not frankly psychotic, parents or relatives, and their influence may be actually detrimental to the welfare of the patients rather than the reverse. As a corollary of this, if one accepts, as I do wholeheartedly, and indeed as Dr Norton does by implication, that what he calls "the changed atmosphere of the hospital" has subscribed to the patients' improvement then surely it may militate against their wellbeing if they are robbed of the props which the hospital affords, unless adequate substitutes at home or in the community are forthcoming.

And what of those schizophrenics who have no homes or no community to support them? In London in particular, with vast, shifting, multi-racial, multi-coloured, and multi-lingual masses, it is by no means uncommon for discharged patients to belong nowhere and so be thrust back on their own resources, which, by virtue of their psychosis, are slender indeed. The problem of this rootless variety of chronic schizophrenic, and, indeed, of others belonging to poorly integrated social groups, cannot be solved by sweeping it out of the mental hospitals under the social mat. Unless and until the community makes adequate provisions for the ex-hospital chronic schizophrenics in their midst – and there is no apparent hurry to do so in spite of the recommendations of the Mental Health Act, 1959 – they will continue to erupt in a variety of ways. Some undoubtedly will find their way back to hospital – some, less fortunate perhaps, will swell the ranks of the unemployed and unemployable. Others will join the army of vagrants and elbow each other off the park benches, or lengthen the queues outside the doss-houses. Others still will embarrass the courts and prisons where their crimes, usually petty and purposeless, unless interpreted as a plea for care and protection, have landed them.

To illustrate this last point I might add that since the beginning of this year I have been called in by prison medical officers under the terms of the new Act and arranged admission to hospital for no less than 17 male prisoners. All of them are seriously disturbed chronic schizophrenics who have been discharged from mental hospitals, sometimes only a matter of a few days before being apprehended by the police. What the total number of such prisoners is in the country as a whole I have no idea, but it must be very substantial.

Unfortunately, the decision as to whether Dr Norton's prognostic optimism in schizophrenia, or my scepticism, is justified is of more than academic importance. On the assumption that he is correct in his views, Dr Norton predicts that the population of mental hospitals will fall by 30% in the next 20 years. Now that the Minister of Health has expressly sentenced the present mental hospitals to destruction, such predictions coming from someone with the prestige which Dr Norton rightly enjoys might accelerate carrying out the sentence. I only hope that the building of other smaller institutions under whatever guise or name they function, but catering, I suspect, for roughly the same number of mental patients as at present, will precede the onslaught of the bulldozers. – I am, etc,

HENRY R ROLLIN

Horton Hospital,
Epsom, Surrey.

The letter brought forth a good deal of wrath, which I had anticipated; but it also earned praise from leaders of the profession whose opinions I respected. I reproduce two letters, one from Dr Desmond Curran, professor of psychiatry at St George's Hospital Medical School, and the other from Dr Henry Yellowlees, formerly physician in psychological medicine at St Thomas's Hospital.

Dear Henry,
   This is just to say how much I liked your letter in the BMJ.
   It was something that needed saying and was well said!
   Yours

DESMOND CURRAN

Dear Dr Rollin,
   My brother, Dr D Yellowlees of Glasgow, recently sent me your letter of April 15th in the BMJ, with the remark that it struck him as "a welcome and unusual change from the blurbs about the marvels of modern psychiatry and the glories of the Mental Health Act".
   I am in an even better position than he to appreciate the letter fully, and I cannot resist writing to say how heartily I agree with him.
   Quite apart from the "window-dressing" of the Act by means of manipulated Hospital statistics and similar devices, *clinical* psychiatry, as I know it and used to teach it, is dead and gone, and it is most refreshing to hear of anyone with the courage to point out that the natural history of an illness – (an expression I haven't heard or read of since I used it constantly in my lectures at St Thomas's) – is a factor in assessing the prognosis.
   I think that your "revolving door" phrase is as true as it is neat, and I offer you my warm congratulations on your contribution, for what they are worth.
   Sincerely yours,

HENRY YELLOWLEES

It might have been argued, as indeed it was argued, that my views were unduly jaundiced and prejudiced and were based on the experience of one hospital drawing its patients from London and were, therefore, an expression of a "metropolitan phenomenon". I hasten to add, however, that even if this were the case the many millions who make up the population of London cannot be ignored and that what may be true for London was probably true for other large conurbations, such as Birmingham, Bristol, Liverpool, Glasgow, and Leeds. It was reassuring, therefore, to have support for my views from two provincial sources.

The first is contained in a letter from Dr Anthony Flood in the *British Medical Journal* in 1963.[8] He wrote: "For the past two years I have been seeing the same problem from another aspect. Of the 200 men whom I have interviewed in a hostel for vagrants [in the Bristol area] 50 had previously been in mental hospitals and of these 26 had been diagnosed as suffering from a schizophrenic illness. In the latter group 18 had been in prison, mostly on more than one occasion. There is, for many chronic schizophrenics in the present day, a trilogy of mental hospital, flop-house, prison, and in that order."

The second is contained in an article written by Gore *et al* in the *Lancet* in 1961 describing the situation in Leeds.[9] They claimed that far from a reduction according to the Hospital Plan in mental hospital beds to 5840 by 1975 it was estimated that the bed needs would be 9000 to 10 000 in their area. They concluded with the same pessimistic note that I had dared to sound: "Patients can be discharged and beds can be emptied, by administrative decision, but, in the absence of some substantial and favourable change in the situation, this can be achieved only at the cost of much hardship to patients and their families."

It is precisely because there was no "substantial and favourable change in the situation" that the National Schizophrenia Fellowship came to be established. In *The Times* of 9 May 1970 an article entitled "A case of schizophrenia" was published. The author was anonymous. Such was the response from relatives of schizophrenic patients, who were just as distressed, perplexed, and overwhelmed by mixed feelings of guilt and impotence as the author was, that an exploratory committee was formed – the "Schizophrenia Action Committee," out of which grew the National Schizophrenia Fellowship. The anonymous author materialised as John Pringle who thus, more by accident than intent, founded the fellowship and from its inception in 1972 until his death in 1984 served as president. He was very ably assisted by Mrs Peggy Pyke-Lees, the first general secretary, and a committee of voluntary workers. The fellowship has the support of the department of social psychiatry of the Institute of Psychiatry, London, whose director, Professor John Wing, together with Professor G M Carstairs, Dr Donal F Early, and myself served as honorary medical advisers.

In the foreword to the first report of the fellowship published in 1974 Mr Pringle does not pull his punches.[10] He castigates those whose duty it was "to provide the community support in replacement for custodial care, which many chronic sufferers [from schizophrenia] unable to find for themselves, cannot do without." He goes on: "The closure of mental hospital wards, which at least provide the basic minimum shelter and life support, goes ruthlessly on leaving nothing in their place."

The body of the report contains a series of accounts by relatives, mainly parents, of what it is like to live with schizophrenia. The burning desire to do what is right shines through the pages, but if there is a common theme it is that there are promises and more promises of help from various agencies, but in the end the relatives are left to go it alone. "The effects of having George at home on our home life has been disastrous," typifies several examples of the way one schizophrenic can wreck the social life of an entire family. "I do not think 'the community' exists," is the sad reflection of a mother whose daughter has encountered "the sneers, no job, cold shouldering, impatience and a general feeling of being out of step." "I have found that every hospital wants to discharge my son at the first opportunity," is a wry comment on current administrative policy which still obtains in so many mental hospitals today. "On three occasions, when she has reacted unfavourably to long lasting injections of Modecate, I have had to call the police as she went berserk and literally threw furniture about," describes very dramatically the unpredictable violence of some chronic schizophrenics. "All of the other colleges have rejected me without interview, and I feel that admission of schizophrenia is being held against me," is the sad comment of a graduate who wanted to become a school teacher. "There is, therefore, virtually nothing available in the way of after care, rehabilitation or training for the schizophrenic in this immediate area," is a caustic statement requiring no further comment.

These direct quotations give weight to the cri de coeur made by John Pringle in his foreword: "Cannot a humane society do better than this for one of the most vulnerable and least befriended sections of its people?" he asks. It can; but if the demands made on the resources of the fellowship, now a widespread national organisation, are any index, it seems clear that there is an enormous amount still to be done.

It is particularly pertinent to quote a piece from the *British Medical Journal* of 15 August 1987. It is headed "MIND on community care" and is a comment on MIND's report prepared for the government's review of community care. It begins "Mental health care is at crisis point. Conditions in many psychiatric hospitals are simply unacceptable, and the community services are not growing nearly fast enough." This alarming statement is made by Lord Ennals, chairman of MIND, who as Mr David Ennals was Minister for Health in the Labour government from November 1968 until June 1970. He must, therefore, be held partly responsible for the mess. Was there ever a better example in political terms of the poacher turned gamekeeper?

Thinking back on the campaign I have waged since 1961 I could, with some justification, smugly pronounce, "I told you so". But the situation is far too serious to permit the luxury of such self-indulgence.

1  *A hospital plan for England and Wales*. London: HMSO, 1962. Cmnd 1604.
2  Tooth G C, Brooke E M. Trends in the mental hospital population and their effect on future planning. *Lancet* 1961; i: 710–13.
3  Cross K W, Yates J. Follow-up study of admissions to mental hospitals. *Lancet* 1961; i: 989–91.

4 Norton A. Mental hospital ins and outs. A survey of patients admitted to a mental hospital in the past 30 years. *Br Med J* 1961; i: 528.

5 Maclay W S. Trends in the British mental health service. In: *Trends in the British mental health service.* Oxford: Pergamon Press, 1963.

6 Rollin, H R. The demand for psychiatric beds. *Lancet* 1963; i: 386.

7 Rollin H R. Prognosis in schizophrenia. *Br Med J* 1961; i: 1104–5.

8 Rollin H R. Social and legal repercussions of the Mental Health Act, 1959. *Br Med J* 1963; i: 786–8.

9 Gore C P, Jones K. Survey of a long-stay mental hospital population. *Lancet* 1961; ii: 544–6.

10 National Schizophrenia Fellowship. *Living with schizophrenia.* Surbiton: National Schizophrenia Fellowship 1974.

# 10 The United States of America

During my adolescence and early manhood, America was to me the Promised Land, and New York the New Jerusalem. This is not really surprising when I pause to consider the overwhelming influence of America and Americans on my own cultural and intellectual development. I devoured American literature almost to the exclusion of its British counterpart: there was nothing, I thought then, to compare with the works of Ernest Hemingway, John Steinbeck, Upton Sinclair, and Sinclair Lewis. I held the same opinion about American playwrights, who had brought such a refreshing vigour into the English theatre. I think back, for example, to Tennessee Williams's *The Glass Menagerie* and *A Streetcar Named Desire*, to the dramatic adaptation of Erskine Caldwell's *Tobacco Road*, and to Clifford Odets's *Waiting for Lefty* and *Golden Boy*. Towering above all his contemporaries was Eugene O'Neill with the deep psychological insights into the human psyche he brought to bear in *Desire Under the Elms*, *Mourning Becomes Electra*, and *The Iceman Cometh*, to name a few. I saw most of these plays, at the tiny Arts Theatre near Leicester Square, which was so active in the advancement of plays at that time considered too avant garde for the commercial theatre. The cinema, of which I was also an ardent devotee, was an American possession with Hollywood its undisputed capital. The advent of the "talkies" in the late 1920s if anything increased the dominance of America over that vast and erstwhile powerful industry.

As for music, one would have had to be stone deaf or to have lived in a cave not to have been aware of the sudden upsurge of music from America. To describe it as "popular" music is, to say the least, patronising. It certainly was popular in that it was hummed, whistled, sung, and played every-where one went: but it was also, by any standards, good music. It flowed in an unending stream from the creative minds of a bevy of remarkable composers who emerged almost simultaneously. They included Jerome Kern, Irving Berlin, Richard Rodgers, and George Gershwin, most of them, like Gershwin, New York Jews, the sons of Russian immigrants. But it was Gershwin who to me was much more than the first among equals: he ranked top of that very exclusive league – and by a very long chalk. I had acquired in the course of my wanderings a portable wind-up gramophone which went with me everywhere. My neighbours in various hostels and hospital lodgings must have been driven crazy by the Gershwin records I played time after time after scratchy time, and in particular his *Rhapsody in Blue* and *An American in Paris*. Even today, as I write, when the 50th anniversary of Gershwin's death is being marked internationally, I have only to hear the wailing glissando of the opening clarinet of the *Rhapsody* to experience the same frisson down my spine as I did half a century ago. I have indelible memories, too, of an early production in London of *Porgy and Bess*, and thinking at the time that the word poignant had been specifically invented to describe the heart stirrings of the soprano aria "Summertime".

Even so, it was, as I have already indicated, with American humour and humorists that I identified myself most closely. My devotion to the Marx Brothers is, and will always be, unfaltering; but next to them in hierarchical order I would place Damon Runyon's lovable rogues. For as long as I can remember I had harboured a burning ambition to eat cheese-cake at the source, at Mindy's on Broadway, where I was convinced I would meet up with Harry the Horse, Dave the Dude, Good Time Charley, or other of my disreputable heroes.

I was sufficiently circumspect, however, not to mention this ambition when, in 1953, I applied for a Fulbright fellowship. I succeeded in my application, and, as luck would have it, on arrival in New York, I had an early opportunity to realise one at least of my fantasies. My visit to Mindy's was, as it turned

The author with his
sister Ethel, circa
1917

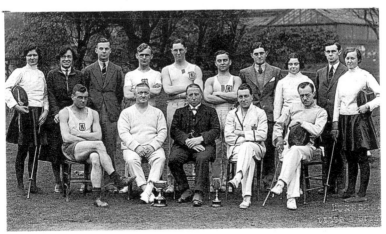

Leeds University Gymnastics Team (which included the boxing and
fencing teams), 1932–3. Author is fourth from right, back row

...the uniform was very becoming

Department of Psychiatry, Temple University School of Medicine, Philadelphia, 1953–4. Professor O S English is second from left, front row; H R Rollin third from left, middle row

Meeting of the Parole Board, February 1971. Clockwise from bottom left: S Bradley, Hon Mrs L Price, S Brown QC, unknown, Mr Justice Waller QC, the Lord Hunt, H L J Gonsalves, clerk, M A Partridge, H R Rollin, R D Fairn. (Crown copyright)

Mr P G Shute and Professor P CC Garnham at the unveiling ceremony of the plaque in the Mott Clinic, 2 June 1975

With Maria, wedding no 1, 27 July 1973

Junior globetrotters: Rebecca and Aron, Penang, Malaysia, 1988

out, doubly enjoyable in that I went there in the company of George Shearing, the blind English pianist who was the star entertainer at a night club to which I had been invited. Shearing, had he been sighted, would have been classed as one of the most brilliant exponents of modern jazz: the fact that he was totally blind lifted him several notches: to describe him, therefore, as a phenomenon, would be no exaggeration. And he was such a very nice person, who asked for no concessions to be made for his handicap. To have heard Shearing play Gershwin as I had done was a consummation devoutly to be wished: to hear Shearing on Gershwin, for whom he had a profound admiration, was another. It was at Mindy's while listening to Shearing with rapt attention that I still managed to survey the scene. To my disappointment I was unable to identify positively any of Runyon's celebrities, but there were a dozen or more who might well have filled the bill. But if there was a modicum of doubt about the identity of some of the customers, there was absolutely no doubt about the quality of the cheesecake.

Nevertheless, the realisation of a young man's fancy was not the sole object of the exercise. The express reason for wanting to study in the USA was to further my growing interest in psychosomatic medicine, a subject which at that time was neglected in the UK. In the States, however, it was undergoing a renaissance due, I think, to the blending of two forces. One was the Meyerian emphasis on psychobiology and the development of the individual in a specific social milieu. The other was Freud's theories on the development of the personality. The methods and conclusions of the American psychosomatists were based largely on hypotheses which were, and still are, treated with some incredulity by organically-minded physicians, even in the States. Nevertheless the intriguing experimental work of Dr Harold G Wolf (whom I was to meet) and his associates in New York had gone a little way towards validating some at least of these hypotheses.

In applying for a Fulbright fellowship one had, for very obvious reasons, to be specific about what and where one wanted to study. I had read as widely as I could and had come to the conclusion that I would, for preference, like to work under Dr Edward Weiss and Dr O Spurgeon English, whose textbook *Psychosomatic Medicine* was accepted as a standard work. Both these physicians were on the staff of Temple University Hospital, Philadelphia, and it followed, therefore, that that is where I would need to go. After due negotiation this was arranged. Included in the academic package was a shortish stint at Johns Hopkins, Baltimore, considered in those days as the finishing school for British psychiatrists. But by the time I arrived, the commonsense psychiatry of Adolf Meyer had, alas, given way to the more esoteric formulations of the psychoanalysts.

I say "alas" because, until I arrived in America in 1953, I had no real appreciation of the extent to which Freudian psychoanalytic theory and practice had taken over psychiatry, at any rate, the psychiatry of private practice and of university centres and hospitals. Added to this was the almost frightening psychiatric awareness of the population at large. There was at the time a veritable flood of Hollywood films in which a psychoanalyst played a major role. The stereotype was a small, bald, myopic doctor, speaking what passed for Viennese English, who in suave measured tones created order out of chaos and, with magical facility, explained the inexplicable. Even language had been influenced: an odd assortment of phrases of pseudo-analytic jargon had been incorporated into everyday parlance. Thus, people no longer got on well together, they "related well to each other", or they were "relaxed and well integrated" when they might well have been described very simply as "rather nice".

The demand for psychotherapy, which was virtually synonymous with psychoanalysis, was enormous and far exceeded the supply of bona fide therapists. The situation was reflected in a New York magazine of the time in which a young, enterprising analyst was shown with a notice on the door of his consulting room (or office), which read "Three couches: no waiting!"

I was to discover, too, that the mode of referral to psychiatrists in America differed radically from that to which I was accustomed. The letter of introduction from the GP or brother specialist was usually missing. An American who, in his own wisdom, considered he should consult a psychiatrist would make his own appointment with a practitioner of his own choosing. Furthermore, it seemed to me, the reasons for such a consultation were much more broadly based. The existence of what were termed "problems" – that is to say, difficulties of a day-to-day sort not causing distress or illness in the true sense of the word – were sufficient to warrant a consultation, or, maybe, the inception of a personal analysis. In all, it was my impression that the American psychiatrist was endowed by the public with an omniscience and infallibility which mercifully has never been the case in Britain.

Lest it should be thought that my alien eye had registered a distorted image of the American psychiatric scene, I call to my assistance no less a personage than Dr John Whitehorn, then head of the department of psychiatry at the Johns Hopkins Hospital, with whom I had discussed my impressions. Most conveniently for me he had previously published the nub of what he told me in his presidential address to the American Psychiatric Association, 1951.[1] He had said: "It has been difficult for many European psychiatrists to understand the American situation. It looks to them as if the psychoanalytic movement has captured American psychiatry. It is true, I believe, that a considerable majority of American psychiatrists have cause to appreciate and acknowledge the great values of certain Freudian concepts and methods which have broadened and deepened the study of many psychiatric problems. In this sense there has been an assimilation of much of psychoanalysis into general psychiatry."

In paying this graceful tribute to Freud, Dr Whitehorn in another part of the same address echoed my own apprehension of things as they were, let alone of things to come. He said, talking of the intense preoccupation of American psychiatrists with the social implications of psychiatry: "Still another aspect of this social interest has been expressed in the zeal to project psychiatric theories onto a broad range of social problems which has sometimes outrun good judgment. It is as if promissory notes had been circulated in the name of psychiatry, beyond our present ability to make good on them."

It is a strange irony, incidentally, that what America owes to Freud would tax the resources of the Institute for Advanced Studies at Princeton to compute, whereas Freud's debt to America could be reckoned in peanuts, as they say. For Freud during his visit to America in 1909 was unhappy, and despite his awareness of the subsequent growth of his teachings there he never changed his coldness towards it. In fact, he is reported by Hans Sachs (1945) in his book *Freud, Master and Friend*[2] to have said, "America is the most grandiose experiment the world has ever seen, but, I am afraid, it is not going to be a success." It will, I believe, be generally conceded that in this instance the Master was well off target.

In general there was much that I found strange by English standards, but a great deal that I found praiseworthy. For example, there was an ever-increasing trend to teach psychiatry not as an encapsulated subject, beginning and ending with the psychoses and neuroses, but to teach in addition the psychiatric implications of the many ills to which flesh is heir. It was in pursuit of this approach at Temple that I was privileged to serve as a member of a team in an investigation into possible emotional factors in the aetiology of coronary heart disease. A paper describing our project and its results was read at the 105th annual meeting of the American Medical Association in 1956 in Chicago (which I attended) and published in *Archives of Internal Medicine* in 1957.[3]

Another decided difference was the virtual absence of formal didactic lectures, which had been largely replaced by conferences. Conferences, in fact, went on all day, every day. Even the lunch hour was not sacred: staff members, because of their commitments at other times, often had yet another conference over a sandwich lunch. The conversion from formal lectures to the much more informal round table conference is a major break with European academic tradition and is, I believe, a step in the right direction. The teacher literally comes down from his pedestal and becomes one of a group, albeit its leader. There is certainly a much greater familiarity between teacher and pupil (first names are the order of the day), but it is not a familiarity which breeds contempt – always provided the teacher can satisfy the demands of the earnest, anxious, hard-working, and somewhat aggressive students he has to instruct.

I was impressed, too, by the elaborate use of recording machines for teaching purposes. The tape machine was ubiquitous and recordings were made, seemingly, of everything – roundtable conferences, psychotherapeutic sessions, group sessions, etc – all of which could be played back and discussed and criticised when the occasion arose. From time to time I was called upon to give a formal, or informal, address to the department or the faculty, and I had little choice but to accustom myself to being stopped in mid-sentence in order to have the tapes changed.

What I found of particular significance was the enormous gap in status between the psychiatry practised in the prestigious university clinics in which I worked and in the state mental hospitals. There was, indeed, a reluctance on the part of those I approached to arrange a visit to one such hospital. With persistence I eventually succeeded and spent a day near Baltimore at a state hospital, which must be nameless for the simple reason that I have forgotten, or more likely repressed, the name. I was not impressed with what I saw. The director who conducted me round was forthright in his condemnation of the conditions in which he had to work and was at pains to point out the overcrowding, the obsolete equipment, and the under-funding which was reflected in the sleazy condition of the furniture and the decoration of the wards. He was particularly condemnatory of the medical staffing. There was, as he demonstrated, an acute shortage of doctors in state mental hospitals and those who were recruited were "not out of the top drawer". Salaries were much lower than those earned by colleagues attached to university clinics or medical schools, and microscopic compared with those earned by successful private practitioners. Perhaps even more important was the fact that their professional status was "less than the dust". What seemed painfully evident from the grim picture he painted was that whereas in England the gap between the mental hospital psychiatrist and his colleagues in the teaching hospital had been decidedly narrowed, in America, as I saw it, the gap had been considerably widened.

That was over 35 years ago. A thought must be spared for the plight of the chronic psychotics in America today, where the policy of "discharge and be damned" finds official favour. At least when I visited them they had a home, inadequate as it was in many ways, and they were cared for, although the standard of care may not have been of the best. But despite all the shortcomings, life for those hapless, helpless, chronically sick people must be infinitely worse now that there is no alternative to the sidewalk, the doss-house, or the prison. The position as it obtains today is aptly summarised by John A Talbott, president of the American Psychiatric Association, who declared in 1984, "Our public facilities are deteriorating physically, clinically and economically: our chronically ill are either transinstitutionalised to nursing homes or deinstitutionalised to our cities' streets."[4]

But it was at Temple University Hospital, located in a rather unsavoury and not entirely safe area of north Philadelphia that I worked for the lion's share of my stay in America from 1953 to 54. My chiefs were Dr Edward (Eddie) Weiss and Dr O Spurgeon (Spurge) English. Dr Weiss was professor of clinical medicine. He had undergone a personal analysis, and it came as no surprise to find that his approach to clinical medicine – or, rather, psychosomatic medicine – was unashamedly psychoanalytically orientated. Dr English was professor of psychiatry and an avowed psychoanalyst.

Temple, therefore, was a temple dedicated to the greater glory of Freud and the Freudians. Like most embryo psychiatrists of my generation I had carried on a mild flirtation with psychoanalysis. I had read a good deal of the literature, some of which I understood and enjoyed and some of which I found either incomprehensible or absurd. I was prepared to subscribe to a certain amount of Freudian theory in that it offered hooks – not necessarily the right hooks – on which certain mental phenomena could be hung. Furthermore, it explained how the workings of the mind in mental illness could be seen as distortions or caricatures of normal mental processes in the same way as rickets or Paget's disease of bone distort the human skeleton.

But this brilliant and inspired theorising is a far cry from psychoanalysis as a therapeutic tool. And the longer I worked at Temple the more sceptical I became and the more convinced that the practice of psychoanalysis was not for me. The clinical meetings, which I felt obliged to attend and at which no patient was ever produced, I found harder and harder to take. To be plunged into this galère was like a boxer suddenly finding himself in the company of all-in wrestlers. There was a ring to be sure, and a face-to-face confrontation; but for the rest, the rules were different, the tactics were different, and the jargon, at first, entirely incomprehensible. I sat for hours in open-mouthed wonderment observing the hair-splitting tussles that were fought out between the faithful over the interpretation of fine points of dogma such as, I imagine, take place among Dominicans, or, perhaps more apropos, among Talmudists. It was during one of these verbal battles that, try as I might, I could not suppress the schoolboyish giggles to which, as I have previously confessed, I am prone. The effect was electric. The chairman glowered at me and in a voice tinged more with anger than with sorrow, growled, "Henry, it may be a joke to you, but to the rest of us it's a religion." And that's precisely what it was; and that's precisely why, having in my life escaped the constrictions of both religious and political dogma, I wished no part of it.

It was fortunate for me that this slight contretemps occurred towards the end of my stay at Temple, although in all fairness to my colleagues I must add that no reference was ever made to it again, and it certainly seemed to make no difference to our social relationships. I would have offered my apologies for my display of bad manners if such had been requested, but they were not. Perhaps it so happened that at some subsequent meeting the incident was "interpreted". If it had been I would have given my eye teeth to have been a fly on the wall and so able to listen to the metaphysical speculation and theorising which would certainly have been evoked.

Having taken my stand vis-à-vis psychoanalysis I have had no occasion to vary it; nor will I. In spite of my views, of which I make no secret, I have good friends on both sides of the Atlantic who are practising analysts, but we are sufficiently discreet not to tread on each other's corns. I have often pondered why there should be this enormous difference in the acceptance of psychoanalytic dogma in our two countries. In this regard I am tempted to quote Jules Masserman, himself an American analyst, but one obviously with a splendid sense of humour. He was asked why it was that in America an analysis lasts two or three years whereas in England "a proper psychoanalysis" should persist for seven, eight or nine years. He replied irreverently that it takes the British that much longer to see a joke.

There are American psychiatrists, analysts and eclectics alike, who manage to retain a healthy realism about the potency of available psychiatric techniques. There are some indeed who are downright cynical. One such cynic wanted to know in the course of conversation what therapies were practised in my hospital "back home". In all innocence I began to give him my list: drama therapy, art therapy, music therapy, occupational therapy – I paused for breath, giving him just enough time to get in his blow, which he delivered with mock severity.

"Boy, you ain't seen nothing. Why, in my hospital, when patients go into the dining-room it's known as eating therapy!"

But I did not live by work alone: I was royally entertained wherever I went. Americans, I am convinced, are the world's most generous, hospitable, and friendly people. On this and on many subsequent occasions I have received nothing but kindness far beyond the call of courtesy. I remember arriving alone and unknown at Johns Hopkins Hospital in Baltimore in the afternoon of 3 July 1963. I can afford to be absolutely certain about time and date because the following day was 4 July, Independence Day, when no one is permitted to be alone and unknown. I checked in at the Dean's office about 2 pm and by 6 pm I had received invitations to no less than four Independence Day dinners, three from colleagues I had just met, and one from the hall porter who showed me round. I had accepted the first of these invitations with extreme gratitude and was embarrassed to have to turn down the other three, particularly the one from the hall porter, an anglophile from way back. He had served in the US Air Force at Brize

Norton and shared my love for the Cotswolds, a love augmented in his case by other loves of a more fleeting kind, to be had at Burford or any of the surrounding villages.

But it was in Philadelphia – the city of brotherly love – that I made the deepest and most meaningful friendships, despite the differences in psychiatric emphasis which may have existed. The department of psychiatry at Temple was made up of an extraordinary polyglot collection of people featuring representatives from the USA itself, from Canada, Hawaii, Brazil, Mexico, Argentina and myself alone from the UK, all welded into a cohesive social unit by the charismatic personality of "Spurge" English. "Spurge" became a close friend with whom I have kept in touch over the years. At the age of 86 he still practises, and never a Christmas passes without I receive a letter in his own hand enclosing a photograph of as many of his ever-increasing family as he can assemble at any one time. Andy Watson, another good companion, is now professor of law and psychiatry at Ann Arbor University, Michigan, and is a splendid example of an exceedingly useful academic hybrid unknown in this country. I saw a good deal of him in London where he spent a sabbatical year, and later enjoyed his hospitality when he invited me to lecture at Ann Arbor. That the personal contact has ceased is entirely my fault. Mea culpa.

Outside the department of psychiatry I was deeply indebted to Eddie Weiss who showed me endless hospitality at his baronial-style home which for very obvious reasons he whimsically called "Mainly Hall". I was to be badly shaken by his sudden and premature death at the age of 64 in 1960 from coronary thrombosis. What was so grimly ironic was that in 1954 he had published a highly successful book aimed at the general public entitled, *Don't Worry About Your Heart*. He had presented me with a copy, on the fly-leaf of which he had generously written, "For my friend and associate Henry Rollin who had much to do with the cultivation of this interest." As a token of my affection and respect I wrote an obituary notice which was published in the *British Medical Journal* on 6 February 1960.

My closest friendship at Temple, however, was forged with

Fred Rogers. The common denominator here was not psychiatry but medical history, on which he is a very considerable authority. He proved to be a patient tutor, and it was as a result of his efforts that I learnt more than a little American medical history. Philadelpia, as he was at pains to point out, was "the cradle of American psychiatry", a cradle that had been rocked by men who bore such immortal names as Benjamin Rush, Thomas S Kirkbride and S Weir Mitchell. It was here in Philadelphia that the first psychiatric outpatient clinic in the world was founded as long ago as 1867, he emphasised with pride. In July 1970 I persuaded Fred to come to London to address the Osler Club. His paper was appropriately entitled "Osler and Philadelphia."

But Fred was more than an eminent professor of preventive medicine and a medical historian of distinction. His interests were wide enough to encompass an enthusiasm for jazz, an enthusiasm which I have always shared. Nothing pleased me more than to accompany him to a particular night spot, Billy Kretchmer's Jam Session Bar in downtown Philadelphia, where for the price of a drink(s) you could listen for as long as you cared to stay to a superlative trio of dedicated jazzmen – piano, clarinet, and drums. The musicians seemed indefatigable and obviously played as much for their own enjoyment as for the entertainment of the customers. I would hesitate to brand their variety of jazz, but their capacity for extemporisation exceeded anything I have heard before or since, even when in New Orleans I realised another of my youthful fantasies and heard jazz at the source. It was in New Orleans, incidentally, that I fulfilled yet another of my inconsequential fantasies: I rode Tennesse Williams's *Streetcar Named Desire*, by then alas, a prosaic bus. Those were still the days of segregation in the South. As a gesture of protest I took a seat at the back of the bus. The conductor, himself black, asked me to move to the front. I declined, protesting that I was quite comfortable where I was.

"OK," he replied wearily. "You don't move; we don't move." I moved; there seemed no other way of resolving what had become an absurd impasse.

As a footnote to my American experience I would add that

on each subsequent visit to the States I have witnessed the undoubted decline in the importance of psychoanalysis. American psychiatrists in the main have become much more eclectic and no longer regard psychopharmacological drugs, ECT, behaviour modification, and the like as heresies. As Fred Rogers, an astute observer of the state of play in the department of psychiatry at Temple, wrote to me as recently as 26 September 1987, "Psychoanalysis is still afforded to suitable patients, but it is no longer paramount as it was years ago."

1 Whitehorn J C. Presidential address of the American Psychiatric Association. *Amer J Psychiat* 1951; **108:** 1.
2 Sachs H. *Freud, master and friend.* London: Imago, 1945.
3 Weiss E, Dlin B, Rollin H R, Fischer H K, Bepler C R. Emotional factors in coronary occlusion. *Arch Intern Med* 1956; **99:** 628–41.
4 Talbott J A. Quoted in: McGovern C M, Hanover N H. *Masters of madness.* London: University Press of New England, 1986: 149.

# 11 The Mental Health Act 1959

My interest in forensic psychiatry was kindled, as has happened not infrequently in my career, by accident and not by design. The "accident" in this case was the implementation of the Mental Health Act 1959 in November 1960, and in particular parts IV and V of the Act which deal with the mentally abnormal offender.

The mentally abnormal offender has, needless to say, always been with us, but the ways in which society has dealt with him have varied from age to age in accordance with the prevailing attitude to the insane and the facilities for their care. Of all the many and complex factors that determine the vagaries of society's attitude to the insane (including those who have offended against the law) it is certain that ignorance and fear, which are closely interrelated, are among the most important. At no time has there been much understanding of the nature of mental illness by the public at large, so that fear, even during times of tolerance, remains latent and can all too readily be brought to the surface. It is then that the fear of the insane, as it is for all others who depart widely from the norm, is translated into oppression. Society has always required its whipping boys as a means of channelling its aggression in a socially acceptable way, or as a means of projecting its own guilt. To this end the feared but nevertheless hapless and defenceless insane are always on hand to be whipped, maimed, pilloried, imprisoned, and burned at the stake as witches, or, as recently in historical terms as 1684 in this country, hanged from the gallows.

What makes the insane such sitting targets is that so much of their overt mental abnormality is manifest in alterations of behaviour and disturbances of thought which, in turn, can be misinterpreted by their judges and be met by them with moral, religious, or legal censure. Not that a man cannot be both mentally ill and guilty of persistent criminal behaviour, or put more succinctly, that he can be both mad and bad; but although one may be unconnected with the other, the two can be confused, a fact of which men of enlightenment have always been aware. Of this, two contemporaneous scholars of the sixteenth century, Reginald Scot[1] and Timothy Bright[2] warned in their writings. The former alluded to the confusion between witchcraft and "melancholia", and the latter between melancholy and sin.

Of paramount importance in the history of the treatment of the insane in England in relatively modern times is the exemplary work of Lord Shaftesbury, which resulted in the passing of two Acts of Parliament in 1845 designed to improve the regulation and treatment of lunatics and the provision and regulations of the lunatic asylums in which they were contained. Although the Lunacy and Mental Treatment Acts 1890–1930 and the Mental Deficiency Acts 1913–1938 have sought to improve the lot of the mentally disordered, the first fundamental revision of the English mental health law since 1845 came with the Mental Health Act 1959. This Act must be regarded, in spirit at any rate, as one of the most humane charters in the chequered history of the care of the insane. Every effort has been made to preserve not only the dignity but the civil and political rights of those admitted to mental hospitals or other institutions. One of the main principles on which the Act is based is that as much treatment as possible, both as inpatient and outpatient, should be given on an informal – that is, voluntary – basis. A measure of the success of this principle is the fact that the percentage of informal admissions among *non-offender* patients in the country as a whole is never less than 88% and is sometimes as high as 96%. There was a further safeguard for those admitted under compulsory orders: application for discharge could be made to the mental health review tribunals set up in every regional hospital board area. Only those on whom a "restriction order" (Section 65) had been imposed were debarred from making an application to tribunals, but even they could apply to the

Home Secretary for their case to be referred to the tribunals.

But despite these eminently praiseworthy improvements in legislation, the mentally abnormal offender continues to occupy an anomalous position. Should he be treated for his mental illness or should he be punished for his offence? In practical terms, should he be disposed of through the mental hospital system or through the penal system? This thorny problem allows of no easy solution, as witness the way in which it has been tackled by society at various periods of history, and in the different ways even today in which the same offender may be disposed of by the judiciary at different times for different offences.

The same mentally abnormal offender may be lobbed over the judicial net and land in the court cared for by the psychiatrist on one occasion and, on another, in that guarded by the prison officer. Once started, such a ping-pong-like sequence may be continued indefinitely. It is true that an attempt was made to call a halt to this bizarre game by the marriage of the two methods of disposal by the creation of psychiatric wings for psychotherapy and other forms of treatment at Wakefield and Holloway prisons, Feltham Borstal, and Grendon Underwood: but these are mere tokens and their contribution to the solution of the overall problem in numerical terms is negligible.

What excited my interest after the implementation of the new Act was the extent to which it had succeeded in solving the problem of the disposal of the mentally abnormal offender. But the longer I worked with the Act the more I became convinced that it had possibly succeeded only in aggravating rather than resolving the problem.

The Act, as I saw it, was based on three fundamental assumptions, the first two being in essence the same as were advanced in favour of closing the mental hospitals (see chapter 9). The first assumption was that the new therapeutic techniques, particularly since the advent of the era of psycho-pharmacology, had elevated psychiatry from a state of relative impotence to one of near omnipotence. The second is that "community care" would largely take over the functions of the mental hospital. And the third assumption was based on the most pathetic of all fallacies, one to which I have already referred – namely, that a man must be either mad or bad: he cannot be both.

I have already described in detail some of the social repercussions resulting from the wholesale discharge of patients from psychiatric hospitals without adequate community care (see chapter 9). Incapable of survival without support, a healthy (or unhealthy) proportion of these patients have been redistributed in the community in various socially retrogressive ways. One particularly undesirable locus of redistribution is the prison where the ex-patients have landed after committing offences, the majority petty in nature.

The developing situation prompted the principal medical officer of Brixton Prison, the most important remand prison in England, to write: "I have been impressed over the last few years by the number of people received into prison for mental observation and reports to court who have been in a psychiatric hospital within twelve months of reception. The figures amount to an alarming total of 384 for 1963. They are often schizophrenics with some residual impairment, psychoneurotics or psychopaths."[3]

The situation described in Brixton Prison was reflected in my own hospital, Horton, which was at the receiving end of a goodly proportion of the increased number of mentally abnormal offenders admitted not only after prosecution (part V of the Act) but as unprosecuted offenders (part IV of the Act). It was the dramatic increase in admissions under both parts of the Act that prompted my research. I would be the first, however, to concede that Horton is in some ways atypical and my results may again be claimed as a "metropolitan phenomenon". Nevertheless, the problems of huge conurbations cannot be ignored.

Resulting from my research I published two papers, one in 1963 and the other in 1965, both in the *British Medical Journal*.[45] The two closely linked investigations suggest several conclusions which can be summarised thus:

1   The undoubted increase in the number of prosecuted offenders admitted to psychiatric hospitals since the implementation of the Mental

Health Act 1959 has been paralleled by an increase in the number of unprosecuted offenders admitted.

2 The two avenues of admission are by no means mutually exclusive. The same offender may be admitted following prosecution on one occasion and without prosecution, that is, as an emergency on another. By and large, it emerges that it is the nature of the offence rather than the nature of the offender which determines the disposal.

3 The most common diagnosis by far was schizophrenia, a mental illness which loomed large in all my conclusions, particularly in relation to the social incompetence of the offenders.

4 A surprisingly high proportion of the offenders had long criminal records. Indeed, the key admission to Horton is only one chapter in a tragic biography, highlighted by collisions with the law, custody, court appearances, remand for observation and medical reports, reappearances in court, and further committals to psychiatric hospitals.

5 The ease and frequency with which offender-patients abscond from a conventional mental hospital illustrates the incompatibility of its two functions, namely, that of a therapeutic community and that of a prison.

6 The post-discharge follow-up, taken together with the previous psychiatric and criminological histories, points to a hard core of mentally abnormal offenders, who are incorrigible in penal terms and incurable in medical terms. The procedure, still current, of shunting them in an almost arbitrary way between one system and the other is an embarrassment to both, and cannot be calculated to operate to the advantage of the offender-patients or society itself.

The publication of these two papers, and in particular the one of March 1963, provoked a good deal of attention in both the medical and lay press. There were comments of considerable length in *New Society* (28 March 1963), the *Evening Standard* (22 March 1963) and the *Guardian* (22 March 1963). But the comment I valued most was contained in a long leading article in *The Times* (25 March 1963), headed "Vicious and Costly Circle". In it very perceptive observations were made, including the one of which I was fully aware, namely, that "Since this is the evidence of only one hospital – one which probably gets more than its fair share of offenders – it must be approached with caution." It goes on, however: "The experience at the Horton Hospital is none the less disturbing . . . . It raises the delicate question of public tolerance, which can be ignored only at the risk of jeopardizing the beneficial intentions of the Act." The final paragraph, which warmed the cockles of my heart no end, reads: "What is essential is to be realistic about the ability of curing those suffering from severe mental illness and about the ability of the community to provide effective after care, whether they come from a mental hospital or a prison. If society is prepared to tolerate the nuisance of crime (mostly petty) committed by inadequate individuals who go the rounds of its public institutions that is another matter, but it ought to realize that the circle is both vicious and costly," the wise man concluded.

What pleased me even more was the prompt note from Sir Charles Symonds, one of the wisest men I have ever known:

Dear Rollin,
    Just a line to congratulate you on your penetrating and logical paper in this week's BMJ. I am sure you are right, and hope that notice will be taken of your observations in official quarters. I am reminded of the early 1920s when it was predicted that as the result of psychotherapy most of the mental hospitals would be able to close!
    With best wishes
    Yours sincerely

                                                                    C P SYMONDS


The vicious and costly circle was, and remains, aggravated by the unwillingness of psychiatric hospitals and the recently established psychiatric units in district general hospitals to admit patients who were difficult or dangerous. In a recent authoritative paper, Dr Peter Snowden deals specifically with this vexed problem. He maintains, and I would be the first to agree, that as a result of this opposition "the Special Hospitals and prisons admitted increasing numbers of patients who would normally have received care in the NHS."[6]

Two government-sponsored groups examined the problem: the Glancy report, 1974, and the Committee on Mentally Abnormal Offenders (Butler report, 1975) both advised the provision of specially designed secure units. Dr Snowden closely examines the progress in building and opening of both permanent and interim secure units up to March 1984. His conclusions are scarcely reassuring. He writes: "It could well be that these permanent secure units will underline a deficiency in service for a further group of underprivileged patients, i.e., those who are not dangerous enough to require the maximum security provided for by Special Hospital but whose illness, because of its chronicity, will be unsuitable for long-term care in RSUs. These chronically mentally ill but minimally dangerous patients are not readily accepted by general psychiatric teams and their plight must lead to further innovation, if they are not to be inappropriately admitted to RSUs, Special Hospitals, and Prisons." Or, he might have added, left to wander the streets and commit further offences.

1 Hunter R, McAlpine I. *Three hundred years of psychiatry*. Oxford: Oxford University Press 1963: 32.
2 Hunter R, McAlpine I. *Three hundred years of psychiatry*. Oxford: Oxford University Press 1963: 36.
3 *Prisons and Borstals 1963*. Report on the work of the Prison Department in the year 1963 (1964). London: HMSO, Cmnd 57. 2381.
4 Rollin H R. Social and legal repercussions of the Mental Health Act, 1959. *Br Med J* 1963; i: 786–8.
5 Rollin H R. Unprosecuted mentally abnormal offenders. *Br Med J* 1965; i: 831–5.
6 Snowden P. A survey of the Regional Secure Unit Programme. *Br J Psychiat* 1985; **147**: 499–507.

# 12 Mental health review tribunals

My published papers concerned with the mentally abnormal offender served as an apprentice's diploma entitling me to admission to what was in the early 1960s a small select guild of forensic psychiatrists – or "psychopenologists," as Americans with their passion for neologisms have styled them.

My acceptance as a forensic psychiatrist was to pay rich dividends. The first was to be appointed as a medical member of the mental health review tribunals from the time they were set up in 1960 until age with stealing steps signalled my retirement in 1983. Under the Mental Health Act 1959 such tribunals consisting of legal, medical, and lay members were empowered to hear applications for discharge from a patient (or his nearest relatives) who was compulsorily detained in mental hospital under section 26 (part IV), or in the case of an offender, under section 60 (part V), where the responsible medical officer, or the managers of the hospital, had declined to order discharge or transfer. If an offender was detained under sections 60–65, a restriction order (imposed if it was thought necessary for the protection of the public), the Home Secretary could refer an application to a tribunal for its advice as to the desirability of leave of absence, transfer to another hospital, or discharge.

Although I did an occasional stint as a member of tribunals at various mental hospitals in the Home Counties, I seem to have been specially earmarked for Broadmoor and it was in that hospital, its raison d'être and its history that I became increasingly interested.

In the nineteenth century criminal lunatics, as the Victorians called them, were cared for in the Criminal Lunatic Asylum at Bethlem Hospital. Conditions in the criminal department there were intolerable and it was during the reign of an outstanding humanitarian, Sir Charles Hood, who was then resident physician, that plans were made to build an entirely new State Criminal Lunatic Asylum at Crowthorne in Berkshire. The asylum would accommodate 600 patients, including, that is, all those then held at Bethlem.

In 1863 Broadmoor Asylum was formally opened. It was clean, airy, spacious, and gloriously located high in the Berkshire hills with a commanding view of the valley below: on a clear day the outline of the Hog's Back miles away to the south in Hampshire can be clearly seen. Women were the first to be transferred from Bethlem, but by July 1864 all the patients, men and women, had been moved. Dr Helps, who had succeeded Sir Charles Hood as resident physician at Bethlem, wrote with ill concealed relief in his annual report for 1864: "The whole of the 112 criminals sent to Broadmoor, arrived at that Asylum without a single casualty, although several of them were most violent and dangerous to themselves or others. In three cases it was absolutely necessary to use handcuffs. We are much indebted to the Authorities of the South Western Railway who successfully made every arrangement for their comfort and safe transit." One of those to enjoy the comfort and safe transit on 26 March 1864 was Daniel McNaughton, perhaps Broadmoor's best-known patient, after whose trial in 1843 the famous McNaughton rules were formulated.

From the time of its inception up to the present day Broadmoor – or Broadmoor Hospital, as those who work there insist it should be called – has rarely been out of the news. It has housed, and continues to house, some of the most dangerous men and women in Britain, and to be concerned with their discharge or transfer is an onerous job. The irony of it is that all who have to do with decision-making at Broadmoor are in a "no-win situation": not to discharge brings forth howls of protest from the civil libertarians; whereas an injudicious discharge resulting in disaster arouses, understandably perhaps, grave public anxiety which the media are not slow to fan. In the late 1960s when Graham Young and Terry Iliffe had murdered after their release from Broadmoor, public anxiety rose to such a pitch that the government had to act. In 1972 the Butler committee was set up under the chairmanship of Lord Butler, a man of great distinction whose appointment was in itself designed to assuage public anxiety. The report of the Committee on Mentally Abnormal Offenders, better known as the Butler report, was published in October 1975. Its far-reaching recommendations, let it be noted, have still to be put fully into effect.

My service on tribunals at Broadmoor and as a member of the Parole Board, not to mention my later work as a Home Office consultant forensic psychiatrist, could not fail to produce in me a somewhat jaundiced view of the human psyche. It is sad, indeed, to reflect that of all living creatures man has the greatest propensity to be in conflict with himself and with others. Aggression, and its counterpart violence, both of which carry distinct overtones of dangerousness, seem to be innate. If this is so – and the evidence is pretty irrefutable – then, given unusual or exceptional circumstances, anyone can behave dangerously. For example, the crime passionnel so often carried out with unbelievable ferocity against a person with whom the assailant has had, or is having, a love relationship, is more often than not at odds with his day-to-day behaviour. And what happens to Tommy Atkins when he is translated into Private Tommy Atkins is the stuff that history books are made of. Add to this human propensity for violence the effects of the vagaries of mental disorder and the prediction of dangerousness in those so afflicted takes on yet another dimension of uncertainty.

Yet it is the prediction of dangerousness that is central to decision-making at Broadmoor and other hospitals. Volumes have been written on this very subject, but the answer, so far, has been a large, shiny, medico-legal lemon. There has been, in other words, a failure to produce some sort of philosopher's stone that would transmute the base metal of educated guesswork into the gold of certainty. Alan A Stone, a professor of law and psychiatry at Harvard University, hammers home the point with characteristic vigour. He writes, "I found the published studies of prediction woefully inadequate, poorly conceived, wrongly interpreted, and below any acceptable standard of scientific research or even solid clinical experience."[1] Patrick McGrath, who was medical director of Broadmoor for the whole period I attended there, and who is a man of incomparable experience in these matters, shares the same opinion. With his customary wit and whimsy he is known to have remarked that only 10% of Broadmoor patients would kill again on discharge and that he would be delighted to discharge the remaining 90% if only someone could tell him reliably who they were.

I enjoyed my 23 years of service at Broadmoor. However, I have to admit that throughout this long period and ever since, I have been haunted by doubts as to the worthwhileness of the elaborate, expensive, and time-consuming exercise in which I had taken part. These doubts are reinforced each time a Broadmoor scandal hits the headlines as the result of which one or more of my good friends and colleagues is unmercifully pilloried. On these sad occasions I mutter to myself, with as much piety as I can muster, "There but for the grace of God go I."

1 Stone A A. The new legal standard of dangerousness: fair in theory, unfair in practice. In: Webster C D, Ben-Aron M H, Hucker S J, eds. *Dangerousness: probability and prediction, psychiatry and public policy.* Cambridge: Cambridge University Press, 1985: 14.

# 13  The Parole Board

Britain adopted parole as an integral part of the penal system as recently as 1967, in contrast with other countries where comparable, but by no means identical, systems have been practised for many years. The philosophical basis of the British system is succinctly stated in the report of the Parole Board (1968), the first of such reports. It reads: "Parole is the discharge of prisoners from custody in advance of their expected date of release, provided they agree to abide by certain conditions, so that they may serve some portion of their sentences under supervision in the community, but subject to recall for misconduct." I was appointed to the Parole Board in 1970 and was to serve for three and a half years during which time the philosophy remained unchanged, but, not surprisingly, there were modifications dictated by experience in the operation of the system as time went on.

The lot of a psychiatrist on the Parole Board is a happy, but by no means an easy, one. The work, albeit fascinating, is heavy as measured not only by the volume of the dossiers he is called upon to read, but also by their dead weight which can turn the scale at 16 lb or more. Parole Board Palsy, a recognised occupational hazard, is a syndrome compounded of elements of Saturday Night Palsy, Writer's Cramp, and Miner's Nystagmus. The condition carries a reasonably good prognosis, but if chronicity supervenes a triad of symptoms make themselves felt. The most obvious is a permanent drooping of the right shoulder – if this is the shoulder from which the specially designed harness is slung. Then there is an increasing and irreversible illegibility of the written word. Finally, there is a deterioration in visual acuity requiring the prescription of spectacles for those never previously in need of them, or the addition of a few dioptres to the lenses of those accustomed to their use.

Each of the dossiers considered – up to 35 at each panel meeting – is a compilation of data from various sources concerning one individual whose deviant behaviour has earned him a prison sentence. The recommendation for parole in the final analysis depends on the resolution by the panel of a triangle of forces representing the law, the environment, and the prisoner himself. The panel itself consists of up to seven members whose attitudes and experience differ widely. Decisions are usually unanimous, but from time to time a vote is taken and the names of the "yeas" and "nays" recorded. Although democratically constituted with each member having an equal say, there can be little doubt that the panel as a whole leans heavily on the three professionals, each of whom represents one of the three forces of the triangle. In my day the lawyers advising on legal aspects were Mr Justice Geoffrey Lane (to become Lord Chief Justice Lane), Mr Justice George Waller, Mr Justice Sebag Shaw, Mr Stephen Brown QC, and His Honour Judge R David – a pretty Olympian collection of luminaries, as their subsequent accelerated progress up the legal ladder would tend to prove. Environmental factors were handled by senior probation officers, of the calibre of William Pearce and S R Eshelby, who included in their brief an opinion on the supervisability of the would-be parolee, or, indeed, the necessity of supervision.

The psychiatrist, who could in my day be N J de V Mather, Maurice Partridge, Ernst Jacoby, John Sawle Thomas, or myself, has the responsibility of taking on the offender as an individual, or, rather, as a "personality." It is for him to offer an explanation in non-technical language as to why the prisoner came to offend, why so often he continues to offend, and what are the chances, if any, of his ceasing to offend. Again, as in the consideration of discharge or transfer by the mental health review tribunals, the vexed but vital question of dangerousness arises. In other words, is the safety of the public put at risk if a prisoner is released prematurely? There is a world of difference, for example, between the hopelessly inadequate, intellectually dull, recidivist who expresses his anti-social behaviour in continuing petty thefts and is no more than an irritating thorn in society's flesh, and the cunning professional safe-blower who is strongly suspected of having committed a string of previous offences. There is a comparable difference between the hitherto blameless, wife-dependent husband who in a one-off outburst of passion kills his faithless wife or her lover, and the aggressive psychopath, the unstable schizophrenic, or the deteriorating epileptic who has killed once and may well kill again. The same grave doubt arises in the case of the compulsive arsonist, or the dangerous sexual deviant whose perverse sexual appetite can be satisfied only by the commission of further perverted sexual acts.

In an attempt to determine where on a continuum between the least and the greatest degree of dangerousness a prisoner belongs, the psychiatrist has only the data provided in the dossier to rely on. This contrasts sharply with the procedure in mental health review tribunals where the psychiatrist is obliged to examine the patient before the meeting and to report on his findings at some stage during the proceedings. The disadvantages of giving an opinion on a "paper patient" are obvious, but logistically it is difficult to see how it can be otherwise.

Nevertheless, for the most part the information provided allows the psychiatrist to make up his mind and offer a positive recommendation which, more often than not, is accepted. There are occasions when further information and/or an up-to-date psychiatric report is called for as, for example, in the following cases:

1   Where an aging man with a nil or light criminological record uncharacteristically commits an offence, particularly if it is of a sexual nature. Can this be explained by the onset of dementia?

2   Where there is in the overall consideration of a particular case what the late Professor Desmond Curran used to refer to as a "strong smell of schizophrenia". Is this scent a true or a false positive?

3   Where there is, as so often there is, an additional problem of drink and/or drugs. The panel so often needs to know what treatment, if any, the prisoner has had, and what are the chances of relapse before the period of licence comes to an end.

4   Where a clue in the dossier has been picked up which may be relevant, such as "treated ECT 'X' Hospital". In seeking further information I found that mental hospitals were usually willing to help and would send clinical summaries or the case notes themselves if politely requested to do so.

As I have already indicated, to work on the Parole Board was to accept a self-imposed sentence of hard work, if not hard labour. There were distinct compensations, however. The venues for the London panel meetings all had their particular charm as, for example, the Home Office in White-hall, or any one of the inns of court. The meetings themselves were enlivened by the high quality of the debates, always serious, but seldom bad-tempered. There was, in addition, scope for as many prison visits as one could find time for: the one I remember best was to Dartmoor – not so much for the prison itself which, apart from its history, is undistinguished, but for its location in that uniquely wild, mysterious, and beautiful sector of England.

But the highest reward came in the shape of an invitation from Lord Hunt (of Everest fame), chairman of the Parole Board, to visit the USA on the board's behalf. This I did in October – November 1972. My brief was fortunately left vague – that is, to take a look at the parole systems in the USA. The States are in many ways anything but united and I realised from preliminary inquiries at this end that there was in actuality one system for each state and then a sort of overlord, the federal system. It was quite obvious that in the time at my disposal I would have to be highly selective and I decided that I would be well advised to focus on two states where I could cash in on my friendship with two distinguished legal academics, Professor Bernard Diamond of the school of criminology of the University of California, and Dean Abe Goldstein of Yale Law School. It was in a way fortuitous that in choosing to exploit the good offices of my two friends I afforded myself the opportunity of inspecting, albeit briefly, the systems in both California and Connecticut, two states long acknowledged as being in the forefront of penological reform. That they were geographically and historically poles apart served to paint the lily just that little bit more.

The negotiations to finalise the details of the tour were long and protracted, and in retrospect I must have strained the bonds of friendship to the limit with my endless letters and inquiries. At no time was there any complaint: the more I asked from them and from a growing number of contacts to whom I had been referred, the more obliging and courteous did my correspondents become. The blueprint was at last completed.

I flew from London to San Francisco on 15 October 1972, pausing for an hour at John F Kennedy Airport in New York, where all passengers were obliged to leave the plane. I mention this detail in particular because what I experienced in that hour symbolically set the scene for the tour itself. Passengers had been requested to take their hand luggage with them. To my surprise this was meticulously searched at the exit barrier where a large notice was displayed offering apologies for any delay and inconvenience and explaining that the search was necessary in an attempt to stem the import of illicit drugs. There was yet another totally unexpected experience on the way back to the aircraft: for the first time ever I was "frisked" and in no uncertain fashion, within millimetres of what might in other circumstances have been construed as an indecent assault. So it was that at my first stop in the USA I was alerted to the ever-growing menace of drugs and violence, particularly the use of firearms, in the pursuit of every conceivable crime including, of course, hijacking.

I allowed myself 24 hours to recover from the disorientation that inevitably results from being translated 6000 miles in about half that time, after which it was go, go, go. Americans are prodigious workers, as the high pressure programmes drawn up for me bore witness. It was a two-way process, however. They were as anxious to compare their problems and methods with ours as I was to compare ours with theirs. On Tuesday 17 October work started in earnest. I visited the headquarters of the Department of Corrections in Sacramento, a brand new, spick-and-span building elegantly furnished and equipped, contrasting almost painfully with the London equivalent in Marsham Street, SW1. I smiled a secret smile as I remembered Geoffrey Lane's wry comment as we peeped into an office during a panel meeting there: "Three in a cell. There should be a law agin it."

I had a long discussion with Dr John E Gorman, chief medical officer, who was beset with the same problems of staff shortages and skimpy budgets as we are. He gave me a run-down on the recent trends in the approach to imprisonment as a disposal of offenders. To illustrate his point he emphasised the reduction in the prison population in California in recent years from 28 000 to 20 000, which he attributed to the impact of probation, the reduction in the length of sentences, and to parole itself. There were, however, other interpretations of this phenomenon, as I subsequently learnt.

After lunch that day I had a brief audience with Mr R K Procunier, the dynamic head of the department, who had yanked himself up by his own boot straps from a prison guard to his present exalted position. His language was rich, fruity, and uninhibited. He made no bones about the problems posed by the rising crime rate and the enormous difficulties of dealing with it.

"Do you know the answers?" he challenged me. He answered his own rhetorical question with, "I'm damned if I do! And if you ever learn them for Chrissake send me a cable," he threw in with a tinge of despair in his voice.

In the afternoon I was driven to what must be one of the most fearsome prisons in the United States. Folsom, a huge gothic building, stands out like a Gustave Doré etching, an architectural anachronism, dominating the otherwise stunning landscape. Secure prisons in the USA, of which Folsom is one, are precisely what they purport to be – secure: infinitely more secure than anything I have come across in the UK. Armed guards in watchtowers are anything but discreetly deployed. No one is trusted and nothing is taken on trust. My bona fides had to be vouched for by members of the Department of Corrections, who accompanied me on my visits. They in turn, although possibly on first name terms with the prison officers on the gate, had to identify themselves. Pockets had to be turned out before we went through a screening apparatus designed to pick out metal objects, presumably guns. The dorsum of the left hand is stamped with a dye invisible to the naked eye, but detectable under ultraviolet light. Then, and only then, is a pass issued: and such is the obvious importance of the document that I clung to mine in grim terror just in case I lost it and might never get out. My angst would have increased tenfold had I allowed myself the thought that I was in the company of some of the most notorious outlaws in the States. Name any major crime in the calendar from armed robbery to murder and you could bet your bottom dollar that someone within easy karate-chop distance from where you stood had committed it.

On leaving the prison I willingly surrendered my crumpled pass. But the invisible stamp I perforce took with me, so adding one more each visit to what must have been in the end a prize collection, a collection I suspect, but have never bothered to check, that time and "Tide" must have long since erased.

The prison itself is the prototype of the old-time American penitentiary, looking for all the world like the set for a movie. The inside of the prison is a vast chasm with five tiers of cells, each, however, with its own toilet and wash-basin. A feature of this, and of all prisons, was the free issue of tobacco – not the best quality – on a help-yourself basis.

San Quentin was the other historical gothic fortress I visited, also redeemed by its exquisite setting on a promontory overlooking San Francisco Bay. My host here was Dr David Schmidt, an almost legendary figure in the Californian Department of Corrections. He joined the department in 1932 and was the first trained psychiatrist to do so. There are now, he told me, 80 "MDs" with a complement of psychologists, social workers, and counsellors. He very adroitly sketched for me the history of the development of psychiatric treatment in prisons, the object of which he maintained should be the establishment of a therapeutic community.

"This does not mean that doctors should condone crime," he insisted, "but that they should be alive to the possibility of treatment during incarceration. Without treatment we manufacture monsters in the prison system," he added. He was, in spite of his idealism, very down to earth and was aware of the fundamental dichotomy still existing between himself and his philosophy and the custodial staff and theirs. His staff at San Quentin, numbering "three and seven tenths" psychiatrists, one psychologist, and three correctional counsellors, was hardly enough to make a diagnosis let alone carry out treatment, he reflected ruefully. There was in the prison a reservoir of violent and sex offenders, 80% of whom, he reckoned, could benefit from psychiatric treatment; but only 20% could hope to receive any.

The emphasis in treatment, both philosophically and operationally, is on group therapy as a means of spreading the available resources. All members of the psychiatric staff, irrespective of their academic disciplines, are involved in group therapy: each therapist will conduct up to nine groups of eight to twelve prisoners per week.

I attended two groups. In each, half the prisoners were white and half black. It was significant perhaps that on both occasions the prisoners arranged themselves on either side of the therapist (a correctional counsellor) according to their colour. The majority of the prisoners had been convicted of crimes of violence: murder, rape, and the use of firearms in the pursuit of crime, for example. By contrast with the external security, the atmosphere within the prison and in the groups themselves was extremely free and easy. The prisoners slouched on chairs, smoked, read newspapers, or devoured veritable mountains of ice-cream. The degree of participation varied enormously; some participated actively in the proceedings, while others remained silent and sullen throughout. Of the former, two virtually monopolised the session. One was a massively built young negro who was very frank in his assertion that he regarded crime, and violent crime if need be, as a way of life. The other was a young white, the victim of a most appalling upbringing, who would easily fit into our diagnostic category of psychopathic personality. It was difficult to see how either case could benefit from this form of treatment, indeed any form of psychiatric treatment; but then I would be the first to admit that, after such a brief exposure to what went on in these meetings, I was in no position to judge.

Vacaville, which I twice visited, stands out in sharp

contrast with the two other institutions. It was built quite recently at enormous expense and symbolises all that is new in the philosophy of the Californian Department of Corrections. It functions, in effect, in three distinct but interdependent ways – namely, for the assessment of all prisoners convicted in northern California; as a psychiatric hospital; and as a prison as such. Vacaville has become the focal point of psychiatric treatment for the state system, and enjoys a far better staff ratio than the other prisons. By law all sex offenders have to have a psychiatric report before being considered for parole, and I was permitted to sit in at one of these screening processes. All who had to do with the prisoner during his sentence, psychiatrists, psychologists, and correctional counsellors, took part in the interview and a consensus report was prepared.

I paid two visits to the headquarters of the Adult Authority in downtown San Francisco. On the first occasion I was invited to join a panel meeting (two members only were present) considering the disposal of parolees. A parolee was not himself invited to attend, and it was evident that the parole officer in presenting his report and making his recommendation determined the action to be taken – that is, revocation, continuation or termination of parole. It is to be remembered that all sentences in California are indeterminate and the Parole Board, therefore, becomes in effect a sentencing authority. The importance, then, of these review committees becomes obvious. It was equally obvious that they were prepared to take far greater risks than we are, and that their deliberations, lasting a few minutes in each case, were seemingly less searching than ours. "He done a real good job for the past year. Let's hope he don't get loaded tonight and blow somebody's head off," was the prayer offered by the parole officer after ordering the discharge from licence of what to me sounded a very doubtful character.

During both visits, however, I took the opportunity of discussing with psychiatrists, psychologists, and parole officers what interested me most – namely, the mandatory attendance of some parolees at psychiatric outpatient clinics, a procedure to which I am fundamentally opposed. Whilst admitting the futility of attempting psychotherapy with an unwilling subject it was pointed out that: continuing attendance and punctuality at outpatient clinics was evidence in itself of the parolee's willingness and ability to conform to a prescribed régime which would in turn influence the Parole Board; the parole agents carried an enormous case-load of about 100 and attendance at the outpatient clinics was an additional means of surveillance. In effect, therefore, the psychiatrist and ancillaries became auxiliary parole agents. For example, if a man for whom drink had been proscribed came to the clinic drunk, then it was a fair assumption that he'd been drinking; attendance at outpatient clinics ensured the continuance of drug treatment, particularly where long-term phenothiazines had been prescribed as part of the drug dependence programme.

What is perhaps paradoxical is that although psychiatry and psychiatrists play an enormously important role at all levels of the penal process, there are no psychiatrists as such who are members of the Parole Board.

It would be idle to suppose that after what at best could be only a superficial glance at a complex system of penology my conclusions, if any, could be anything but tentative. Even so, what conclusions I had arrived at, tentative or not, were thrown into confusion by my discussions with academic lawyers, forensic psychiatrists ("psychopenologists", may I remind you?), and criminologists at Berkeley. They viewed all the alleged advances with extraordinary cynicism. They saw, for example, the run-down of the Californian prisons as a political and/or economic expedient. They saw group therapy in prisons as a "two-way con operation": the executive judged cooperation in the programme as a willingness to change, which would commend itself to the Parole Board. The prisoners, on the other hand, knew that non-participation in the programme would be interpreted as an unwillingness to change and, therefore, they played along without any real involvement in the therapeutic process.

They gave cogent reasons for blunt non-cooperation on the part of prisoners – that is: bloody-mindedness; suspicion, particularly by blacks, that the whole operation is white and middle-class, and therefore not meant for them; as a protest of innocence for the crime for which they had been convicted and imprisoned; suspicion that there might be a feedback of information to the authorities. It was indeed difficult to see from my own observations how this suspicion could be allayed. Finally, they explained the prevalence and popularity of group therapy on the basis that a low staff : prisoner ratio prevents any sort of dialogue between staff and prisoners as is to be found in English prisons. This was in accord with the impression I gained of a distinct remoteness between prison officers and their charges.

In Connecticut I virtually duplicated the same programme I had carried out in California. There was one most important addition, however – namely, the opportunity afforded me by the chairman of the Connecticut Board of Parole, Mr J Bernard Gates, to sit in on panel meetings at three prisons: Somers, a maximum security; Enfield, a minimum security; and Niantic, a women's prison. In the men's prisons the incidence of violent and/or drug (overwhelmingly heroin)-associated crimes was exceedingly high; but, alarmingly, virtually *all* the women considered were guilty of drug-associated crimes. Although these were obviously not valid samples statistically speaking, it would be impossible nevertheless to overestimate the importance of violence and drugs as factors in crime in the USA.

There are obvious similarities between the two American parole systems and the British system, but of much greater interest are the differences. In the USA the panels are limited to three members appointed by the governor of the state, although if need be they may function with two. The dossiers are enviably light and appear to average eight to twelve pages. There are no designated disciplines making up the parole boards as we have. The panel meetings are held in the prisons where the prisoners are serving their sentences, and prisoners are obliged to attend in person wherever possible. Ever since I became involved in parole I have pondered the advisability of the prisoner having to appear in person. I am almost sure, after witnessing the procedure in the States, that his presence may not be essential. As one of the panel put it, "It can be to a large extent a slick-salesman operation, in which the less outgoing prisoner may come off badly." A tape recording of the entire proceedings is made. About 20 cases are heard in any one session. In effect the panel retries the case and seems to arrive at its own verdict which may or may not coincide with the judicial verdict. After the hearing the prisoner is dismissed, and after a relatively brief discussion a decision is arrived at, whereupon the prisoner is recalled and told his fate. The chairman may then take it upon himself to give fatherly advice to the prisoner, or conversely, to deliver a homily. If parole is denied, the prisoner is given reasons.

There are two fundamental differences which need emphasis, however.

The first relates to the Parole Board in Connecticut and in California as an effective sentencing body. This function stems from the award by judges in California of indeterminate sentences, and in Connecticut of minimum and maximum sentences which may range widely as, for example, from three to fifteen years. The second is seen in the very high percentage of paroles granted. In effect, all prisoners are paroled at some time during their sentence. The liberal policy has to be evaluated in terms of the high rate of parole failure, running at that time at about 50%. This rate would be unacceptable in the UK, particularly taking into account the gravity of some of the current offences and the seriousness of the criminal records of a not insignificant number of the prisoners.

# 14 Consultant forensic psychiatrist

My metamorphosis from consultant psychiatrist with a part-time interest in forensic psychiatry to consultant psychiatrist with a full-time interest in forensic psychiatry was determined by yet another accident. In this particular instant the accident was the sudden and tragic death in August 1977 of Dr Peter Scott, one of the founding fathers of the contemporary school of British forensic psychiatry and, at the time of his death, possibly its outstanding member.

Peter had divided his time between the Maudsley Hospital, where he was a consultant, and HM Prison, Brixton, where he held an appointment as special consultant to the Home Office. At Brixton he was allocated only cases remanded in custody charged with serious crime, particularly murder. In this capacity he had personally examined well over 200 male murderers and had appeared as an expert witness in innumerable murder trials. His unexpected departure from the scene left a gap in the ranks of experts in this most difficult and highly responsible area of medico-legal work.

Dr Ian Blyth, the then principal medical officer at Brixton, phoned me out of the blue one day, explained the grave problem he was faced with, and asked if I would be prepared to help out by doing a few sessions on a temporary basis until a more permanent arrangement could be made. He had turned to me because he knew I had recently retired from the NHS and might be looking for a part-time job. Although at that precise time I was not exactly kicking my heels, I was nevertheless haunted by a deep-rooted fear of withering on the vine as I had seen so many of my colleagues do after retirement. The offer of employment, albeit daunting in its very nature, was most opportune and I gratefully accepted.

I began my new job at Brixton almost immediately on an agreed basis of four sessions a week and continued so to do for the next three or four years. However, as so often happens in the Civil Service, someone, somewhere along the line, discovered the intolerable irregularity of a temporary employee such as myself continuing to fill a permanent post. The machinery therefore was set in motion to regularise the irregularity. I was duly warned that my job would have to be advertised, but was given the assurance that I was at liberty to apply. A nod was as good as a wink, and so yet again I found myself having to go through the whole application procedure, including the ordeal of waiting in waiting rooms before the final interview. The major difference on this occasion as compared with, say, that at Nuffield College, Oxford, was that I knew personally all the interviewees and all the interviewers. The interview was virtually anxiety-free and, if truth be told, something of a charade – but the regulations demanded that it be gone through. Confirmation that my application had been successful came in an official letter a week or two later.

I continued to work exactly as I had been doing, with this important difference, however, that I could now describe myself officially as "Consultant Forensic Psychiatrist to the Home Office," a description which tripped prettily off the tongue when I was asked, as a matter of routine, to list my qualifications in the witness box prior to being cross-examined.

On my 75th birthday, 17 November 1986, after almost 10 years, I resigned my appointment, not that the job was beyond me – in my opinion at any rate – but for other rather complex reasons. To begin with, I felt that I should make way for younger men I knew to be waiting in the wings. Further, there were and are loose ends in my life that I require time and leisure to tidy up. But the most important reason by far was that I felt an urgent need to start to learn to read again. The fact is that for the past decade, although I had written prolifically, I had become an illiterate. I had read virtually nothing apart from books and journals of a professional kind and books and papers sent to me for review. But the most time-consuming job by far had been reading the committal papers in the cases I had examined at Brixton. These consist of records of interviews with the accused by the police, witness statements, probation officer reports, social reports, medical reports, forensic reports, and the like. The dossier in total may run to several hundred pages which have to be perused, abstracted, and the salient points included in the final psychiatric report submitted to the Central Criminal Court, Old Bailey. Barristers, I soon appreciated, have an uncanny memory for detail and one cannot afford to be caught napping under cross-examination.

The 10 years or so that I spent exclusively in the practice of forensic psychiatry were for the most part rewarding both professionally and financially in that the additional income provided a little butter – even jam – to spread on the dry crust of an NHS pension. The experience I gained was unique: I examined, quite literally, hundreds of men accused of murder, not forgetting a scattering of others accused of offences for which life imprisonment is the maximum possible sentence, such as manslaughter, rape, robbery, and assault occasioning grievous bodily harm. The nature and gruesome details of some of these offences were so spine-chilling as to fill the headlines and untold column inches of every newspaper in the land for as long as the accused was on trial. The appetite of the public for the unspeakable is apparently insatiable. There can be very few doctors, in fact, whose clinical practice has been so well advertised and so well documented as mine has been, sufficient in quantity to fill boxes of newspaper cuttings which, if nothing else, serve as a reminder of this grisly yet captivating chapter of my life.

One consequence of being steeped in crime, and very serious crime at that, was that I was compelled yet again to reflect on the least desirable facets of the human psyche, particularly man's innate potential for violence, and as a corollary, the inherent dangerousness of all men. Once again, as I had been when a member of the Parole Board or the Mental Health Review Tribunal, I was obliged to offer advice, this time to a court of law, as to the dangerousness of the mentally abnormal offender I had examined. Should he be be disposed of in accordance with the due process of law, or via the provisions of the Mental Health Act? If the latter, should it be to a conventional mental hospital, to a medium security unit, or to a special hospital – Broadmoor, for example?

On what body of knowledge was I able to draw on in order to give advice on this vitally important matter? There are, as I had long since discovered, no absolutes in assessing dangerousness. What I was able to offer now was, after all, only an opinion, an opinion which has been based in times past on different sets of criteria, all of them, let it be said, somewhat arbitrary. Shakespeare's Caesar attributed Cassius's dangerousness to his lean and hungry look, thus possibly anticipating by some three centuries Lombroso and Bertillon. The constitutional approach has now been largely discredited: there is no way, in other words, that the mind's construction can be found in the face or in the body build. What has never ceased to astound me, in fact, is how very ordinary in appearance men guilty of the most horrendous crime can be. One is driven back to the conclusion that one factor common to all murderers, or rapists, is that they have murdered or raped. These malefactors, contrary to popular belief, are people; dangerous people, but people, nevertheless. The mark of Cain, if it exists at all, is very cunningly concealed.

Today the assessment of dangerousness is essentially based on psychiatric opinion, and ruefully one has to admit that there is no magical formula available. One does one's best in the full knowledge that one may well be wrong. Experience may improve one's predictive score: it may also bring with it a large chunk of humility.

As a spin-off from my work at Brixton I have been required to give evidence in the guise of an expert witness in many crown courts up and down the land, but in particular, in the Central Criminal Court, Old Bailey. There I had the doubtful distinction of being known by name by security officers, gaolers, ushers, and the staff in the taxation office – not forgetting the canteen, where possibly the worst food in London is served at exorbitant prices. Over the years I have come to know personally and to respect most of the leading

Treasury counsel appearing for the Crown in criminal cases, and one by one I have seen them disappear upwards in a cloud of silk to graze in more lush legal pastures.

For anyone with a feeling for the theatre, to give evidence in any court at the Old Bailey has a distinctly dramatic appeal: but this is extended to infinity in the case of the most famous criminal court in the world, No 1 Court. I have no idea of the exact number of times I have appeared in this particular court, but it certainly runs well into double figures. On each occasion I have been acutely alive to the fact that I am centre stage, an actor in a human drama on which, for the time the trial lasts, the eyes of the world are focused. Like all actors I am aware of the occasions when I have given a good performance and of those when, in other circumstances, I would have been given the bird.

In the course of my forensic career I have been cross-examined by most of our eminent criminal lawyers. This is not always a pleasant experience – far from it. I appreciate, of course, that it is an accepted tactic of counsel to discredit witnesses, but this is a far cry from their deliberate humiliation, which is what certain of the Old Bailey bully-boys set out to do, and often succeed in doing. So savage and relentless is the attack sometimes that I have been made to feel that I am in the dock rather than in the witness box doing my earnest best to assist the court to arrive at a just verdict. This is an unsatisfactory state of affairs because, as things stand, there can be no doubt that the fragile discipline of psychiatry is no match for the heavyweight onslaught of the lawyers. To survive as a forensic psychiatrist, therefore, demands nimble wits and a very tough hide indeed.

My experience as a forensic psychiatrist is unique in one other respect: I am the only one of my calling ever to have been the principal witness at the Old Bailey in a trial where the charge was one of attempted murder and the victim of the attempt was himself.

My assailant, a young and mountainous black man, who had in his time been a professional boxer, was charged with the murder of a fellow patient in a London mental hospital. He had been remanded to Brixton prison for medical – that is, psychiatric – reports and I had been requested to carry out an examination. I did so alone in the same way as I had done in scores of previous cases. It needed no great expertise to determine that he was floridly psychotic, and the disposal to be recommended seemed obvious enough. I was about to terminate the examination when, out of the blue, he very politely asked if he could wash his hands in the basin located behind me and to my right. I thought this was a strange request, but on the face of it it seemed innocuous enough. I told him to go ahead. He made his way to the basin and he did actually go through the process of washing his hands. At least I can remember hearing the water being turned on and then turned off. He had begun the return journey when I was aware that he had suddenly stopped immediately behind me. Intuitively I sensed danger, but before I could take any sort of action, evasive or otherwise, he had wrapped an arm like a steel hawser round my neck and lower jaw and was pulling it hard with the other. I was physically overwhelmed and totally incapable of defending myself. The alarm button was out of reach and the only remaining option was to yell for help which I proceeded to do with all the breath left in me. Fortunately, the officer who had escorted the prisoner and was waiting outside the door of my office, heard my yells and burst in. By this time I was on the floor and beginning to lose consciousness so that the details of what happened thereafter are only dimly etched on my memory. What I do remember and, indeed, shall never forget as long as I live, is the eerie feeling of calm that came over me as I accepted the inevitability of what I was powerless to prevent. In my mind's eye I saw my wife and children and, in so far as I was capable of registering any emotion, it was one of pity; not pity for myself, but an overwhelming pity for them.

What happened afterwards, I learnt subsequently, was that the alert officer who had heard my calls for help was unable to release the assailant's grip on me; but he was able to push the alarm button which, in accordance with a well rehearsed drill, brought an immediate posse of officers to the rescue. Once able to breathe freely I quickly regained full consciousness and my first recall is of a great hulk of a man being carried unceremoniously face down, one officer to each of his four limbs.

I sustained little in the way of physical injury, apart, that is, from scratches on my chin and round my mouth together with considerable bruising of the strap muscles of my neck and lower jaw. My psyche, however, at some level took a bit of a battering, and to this day I have recurrent nightmares in which, in a variety of dramatised versions, I live through the details of my narrow escape in the very same way as so many of my patients relive their traumatic war experiences.

At the trial, during which no one present, judge and jury alike, was left in any doubt as to the accused's mental state, he was found not guilty of attempted murder, but guilty of the lesser charge of assault occasioning actual bodily harm (the original charge of murder of a fellow patient was "left on the file"). The finding of guilt in the case concerning myself allowed the learned judge, in the light of the manifest madness and dangerousness of the accused, to make a hospital order (section 60, Mental Health Act 1959) together with a restriction order (section 65) without limitation of time. He was transferred with the minimum delay to Broadmoor where, I learn on the highest authority, the continuing unpredictability of his assaultive behaviour causes him to be treated with the utmost caution. From all the evidence which has accrued before, during, and after the trial, it became increasingly obvious that this is a rare example of a man who, for no matter what reason, psychotic or otherwise, enjoys killing people. And such men, I have no hesitation in proclaiming, are dangerous.

The assault caused grave concern to the prison authorities, as a result of which immediate action was taken at Brixton and elsewhere to minimise the risk to medical officers. In particular, steps were taken to ensure that prisoners cannot get behind the examining doctor; that an alarm bell (or bells) must be easily accessible; and that help must be readily available at all times – all very simple and commonsensical precautions which I had often preached to others in my lectures and writings, but which I had lamentably failed to take cognisance of myself.

One further lesson to be learnt from this eventful history, particularly for those sufficiently insouciant not to have learnt it very early on in their career, is that the practice of medicine can be a very dangerous occupation.

# 15 Oxford

Much as I prized my appointment to the Mental Health Review Tribunal and the Parole Board, the most glittering prize by far to fall into my lap was my election in 1963 to a research fellowship at Nuffield College, Oxford. For anyone with my parochial background, the opportunity to seek the truth in the groves of Academus stopped short at the portals of Leeds University. Oxbridge was for others; for an intellectual or social élite to which on neither score did I consider I belonged.

I owe my academic elevation, as I do so much else, to Nigel Walker, who was at that time university reader in criminology at Oxford and a fellow of Nuffield College (he was soon after to be elected Wolfson professor of criminology at Cambridge). Walker was then in the thick of conducting the Oxford Survey, an investigation into all hospital and guardianship orders made under the Mental Health Act 1959 in English and Welsh criminal courts from April 1963 to April 1964. With his customary sharp nose for scientific papers which impinged on what he was about, he had read and digested my paper published in the *British Medical Journal* of 23 March 1963.[1] He had immediately written to me inviting me to Oxford for a discussion of topics he thought might be of mutual interest. I seized upon the invitation with almost unseemly haste — which, as it so happens, was just as well.

In the course of conversation with Walker I mentioned, almost en passant, that I had accumulated a mass of data sufficient for a book, but that the lack of time and facilities made it highly unlikely that it would ever be written. Walker reflected just for a moment and then asked if I had ever considered applying for a research fellowship, and went on to explain that the Gwilym Gibbon fellowship at Nuffield was one for which he thought I might be eligible. He might, as far as I was concerned, have asked me if I had thought of applying for the Chiltern Hundreds, or some other ridiculous hunk of pie-in-the-sky. I replied quite simply, but with complete honesty, that such a consideration had never entered my mind. However, if he thought it worthwhile I would make inquiries from the powers-that-be at my end into the feasibility not only of making an application but of taking up the fellowship in the event, remote as I considered it to be, of being elected.

Time was short if the application was to be received in time for the academic year 1963–4. There was a good deal of lobbying to be done among members of the Horton Hospital management committee, an admirable body with whom I was on excellent terms. They were not only sympathetic but positively encouraging. Even more important was the need to seek the agreement of my consultant colleagues at Horton on whom the burden of my absence would fall: they too gave my proposal their blessing. Armed with all this good will I approached the last and highest hurdle, the regional hospital board. Whether it was the prestigious nature of an Oxford fellowship, or my own chutzpah in asking permission to take up a fellowship, bearing in mind that I had enjoyed an equal privilege in 1953 when I was elected to a Fulbright fellowship, I know not. All I do know is that with astounding alacrity not only did they consent but wished me the very best of luck with my application.

With only a few days to spare I sent off my application, burning with high hope but little else – and waited. After a decent (or indecent) interval I was notified by Nuffield that I had been selected for interview. My hopes rose, but when I reread the letter, the actual day set for the interview rang a disquieting bell, and one glance at my diary confirmed that on that selfsame day I was scheduled to assist at a mental health review tribunal at Broadmoor. I immediately phoned the Warden's secretary at Nuffield and explained my dilemma. She made sympathetic noises, but firmly, politely, and for very good reasons, made it clear that nothing could be done. The date was immutable. If I failed to turn up my name would be automatically struck off the list of candidates. With some understandable trepidation I then phoned the secretary of the tribunal, who without a moment's hesitation told me not to worry and to go ahead.

"In this business one is always having to make contingency arrangements," he reassured me. I heaped blessings on his head and breathed again.

There were five or six, maybe seven candidates, summoned for interview, but who my rivals were I never did find out. Minimal courtesies were exchanged as one or other of us entered the waiting room, after which silence reigned – an anxious silence broken only by the rustle of newspapers in which each of us had buried himself. For myself, the protective layers of maturation and sophistication which should have thickened over the years proved to be tissue-paper thin. The forthcoming ordeal was tantamount to a viva, and reflexly, all the inner torment attendant on waiting for vivas which had plagued me since my undergraduate days, resurfaced. As I went into the interview, which had by now assumed the proportions of an inquisition, I urged myself not to let anxiety rule my tongue as it had done so often in the past. So much so had this been the case that there had been times when in a bizarre, dissociated way I was able to listen to myself babbling nonsense and yet, for reasons not easily understood, be incapable of doing anything about it. On this occasion, however, I seem to have heeded my own counsel. I was awarded the fellowship.

In October 1963 I went up to Oxford, and at the ripe old age of 52 matriculated for the second time, was granted MA status and permitted to wear the appropriate academic gown. I was more amused than miffed by one particular example of Oxonian snobbery: because my doctorate had not been awarded by Oxford it could not be officially recognised. My name, therefore, at the foot of the staircase leading to the set of rooms in college which went with my fellowship, appeared plain and unadorned as MR H R ROLLIN.

My year at Oxford was an experience prized far above rubies, affording me as it did a time for work, a time for thought, and, if time remained, a time for pleasure. My primary objective was to complete the book which had been germinating in my mind for some time, the framework of which I had laid down in my earlier papers. This I did: *The Mentally Abnormal Offender and the Law* was subsequently published in 1969.[2]

I worked for some of the time in close cooperation with Nigel Walker and Sarah McCabe, his research officer on the Oxford Survey. Together we published *The Offender and the Mental Health Act*.[3] Again, as a spin-off from our collaboration, Walker and I jointly suggested that one of the Ciba Foundation's small international symposia be devoted to the problem of the mentally abnormal offender. The conference was designed to be interdisciplinary and international and was to include psychiatrists, psychologists, sociologists, and penologists. The symposium was eventually held from 3 to 6 July 1967, at the foundation's premises in London. The chairman was Sir Charles Cunningham and the membership drawn from the UK, USA, Sweden, Denmark, Belgium, Holland, and Bulgaria. The proceedings of the symposium were published in 1968 under the title *The Mentally Abnormal Offender*.[4]

What I found particularly intriguing about Oxford was the efficiency of the academic grapevine. I had no official teaching responsibilities, and yet as soon as it became known that I was in residence (I'm quite sure that this was the experience of others similarly placed) I was inundated with requests to participate in symposia, or to give formal or informal lectures to a variety of undergraduate societies or other student bodies including theology students and probation officers. In addition, I undertook a regular course of lectures at Ruskin College, which I was to continue for some years after I went down. All this academic activity ate into the time available for my own work, but I was delighted and flattered to be of service. Apart from all other considerations, I was given the opportunity to lunch or dine in at least a dozen colleges of high or low degree, at high or low table. Other rewards came my way, as for example, my election to membership of the senior common room at Lincoln at the instigation, I'm sure, of my good friend David Goldey, then Dean, in return for services as unofficial psychiatric adviser to the college.

Nuffield itself is one of three colleges which admit only graduates as students. All Souls was at that time for men only, but St Anthony's and Nuffield opened their doors to men and women. Competition for admission is fierce and applications are received from the world over. Academically, the emphasis is on social studies, which includes economics and politics (psephology, the study of voting, was born and continues to be nurtured here). The academic staff is star-studded: some of the dons, David Butler, Hugh Clegg, and A H Halsey, for example, are household names. Taking into account the academic goodies on offer and the quality of those who dispense them, it is really not surprising that one became accustomed to meeting officially at dinner, or unofficially in the senior common room, ministers of the Crown, ex-prime ministers, an assortment of MPs and captains of industry, some of whom, it was rumoured, had sneaked in for a quick tutorial. Some wag is reported to have said that there are more corridors of power in Nuffield than in Whitehall. In retrospect the greatest benefit I derived from my Oxford experience was the opportunity it gave me to sharpen my wits on the whetstone of some of the finest brains in the country.

*　*　*

Music, I venture to repeat, has always been one of my consuming passions, and it was in the context of music that I was able to make a token contribution to the common weal of the college. Shortly after I had taken up residence I was musing over my soup at dinner one evening when it occurred to me, like a revelation in a minor key, how eminently suitable the hall was for the presentation of intimate recitals by soloists, duos, or small ensembles. Francis Seton, a fellow of the college and himself a pianist of near-professional standing, was sitting on my left. I turned to him and asked him if the college boasted a music society, or had ever held concerts in the hall. To both questions his reply was in the negative. Why not? He didn't know; but he thought that the answer might lie in the simple fact that no one had put forward the idea. Later that evening over coffee the two of us approached Freddie Madden, also a fellow of the college and another music buff, and asked him if he would support the formation of a college music society. He beamed his approval, and they both undertook to place the proposal before the governing body at its next meeting. Approval was, I understand, by no means unanimous; but at the end of the day the Philistines were routed. A modest subsidy was agreed, but for the rest, the fledgling society would have to balance its books by the sale of tickets.

My contribution to the enterprise was to act as impresario. It was my good fortune to have close friends in the big world outside who were professional musicians, and it was this friendship that I unashamedly exploited in the interests of my new-found job. It was self-evident that if the society was to succeed then the inaugural concert would, literally and metaphorically, have to strike the right note. I turned to a particularly dear friend, Olive Zorian, arguably the best woman violinist in England at the time, who was to be tragically struck down in her prime by cancer in May 1965. She, in her typically generous way, agreed to help and forthwith approached the other members of her distinguished string quartet, the Zorian Quartet, who with the same alacrity and generosity agreed the date and the fee – well below the fee they could justifiably command.

The concert, held in the Hilary Term 1963, was not only a huge success artistically, but it set the standard and pattern for the future. The atmosphere was just what I had hoped it would be – intimate and salon-like. The audience, drawn from members of the Music Society and their friends, were seated in comfortable chairs ranged informally round the platform which, incidentally, had been built by the college carpenter. The team effort was further exemplified by Mr Smith, the college butler, an unsuspected aficionado, who proved a tower of strength. He it was who oversaw the preparation of the mulled claret available to all at the interval, and the sandwiches and coffee served in the senior common room where members of the Music Society and their friends had an opportunity to meet the artists after the concert.

For some few years after I came down I continued in my role of impresario. Among the artists who gave their services – and "gave" is probably le mot juste considering the pittance they agreed to accept in the interests of what they saw was a worthy cause – were the Allegri Quartet, the Oremonte Trio, the clarinettist Thea King, and the pianists Rafael Orosco (a winner of the Leeds International Piano Competition), Yonty Solomon, and Anthony Goldstone. It would be churlish of me not to acknowledge the debt owed to my good friend Maria Diamand, one of London's leading piano coaches, for her introduction to this clutch of brilliant pianists and to Bruno Schrecker, the cellist and anchor man of the Allegri Quartet, who, incidentally, was made an honorary member of our society in recognition of his services.

I don't know, incidentally, what professional impresarios' terms of reference are but I doubt if they are as comprehensive as mine were as an amateur. Included in mine as a routine were those of chauffeur and valet, but if occasion demanded, as it did not infrequently, they were stretched to include that of psychotherapist – musicians, no matter how experienced, are not immune from anxiety. But my greatest triumph was in a needle-in-a-haystack exercise, namely, in the first place, to locate the tuner for the piano hired from Taphouse on a Saturday afternoon and, in the second place, to winkle him out of the crowd when Oxford United were playing at home.

When I finally laid down my office I was made the first honorary member of the Music Society. My wife and I receive invitations to all college concerts and as often as is possible we accept. It is most gratifying for me to see that the society has flourished and that the quality and style of the concerts laid down 25 years ago in 1963 have been fully maintained. Not only this: to belong to an Oxford college is to belong to a family – and it is always nice to go home.

1 Rollin H R. Social and legal repercussions of the Mental Health Act, 1959. *Br Med J* 1963; i: 786–8.
2 Rollin H R. *The mentally abnormal offender and the law.* Oxford: Pergamon, 1969.

3 McCabe S F, Rollin H R, Walker N D. The offender and the Mental Health Act. *Medicine, Science and the Law* October, 1964; 231–44.
4 De Reuk A V S, Porter R, eds. *The mentally abnormal offender: a Ciba Foundation symposium.* London: Churchill, 1968.

# 16 The Royal College of Psychiatrists

My career in psychiatry has been played out for the most part against the backcloth of the Royal College of Psychiatrists and its predecessor, the Royal Medico-Psychological Association, familiarly known as the RMPA. I dutifully joined the latter in 1939, but the outbreak of war that year put a damper on its activities as it did on those of all learned societies. It was not in fact until 1957 that I began to be concerned with the affairs of the association – and this was a concern more thrust upon me than sought after.

It so happened that in 1957 I joined a RMPA study tour of Israel. Edward (Teddy) Stern was at that time secretary of the study tour subcommittee and as such it fell to him to organise whatever tours were undertaken. Teddy had done the job for some years and felt for understandable reasons that the Israeli tour must be his swansong. He resigned; and by the exercise of something best described as force majeure I found myself his successor.

As I was soon to discover, it is a job not without responsibility and one bristling with traps for the unwary. But there are compensations, not the least of which is the scope it gives for some degree of self-interest. It falls to the secretary to choose the venues for the tours: I chose in turn Denmark, France, Mexico (coinciding with a meeting of the World Psychiatric Association), and Italy, all of them high on my personal list of priorities. Additional bonuses are to be found in, for example, the privilege as the de facto leader of the group of sitting with one's spouse at high table at formal dinners and luncheons, or of being the first to shake the hand of the host at official receptions. Privilege, however, has always to be paid for in one currency or another, and on these occasions payment was extracted in the obligation demanded by courtesy to reply to addresses of welcome, or to toasts to the guests, ordeals which would tend to remove the gilt from the gingerbread, or, more appropriately perhaps, the parmesan from the spaghetti.

I enjoyed my stint as tours operator, the more so because I became increasingly convinced of their importance, not only as a means of advancing knowledge but as a means of promoting international understanding and good will. So deep is my conviction that I would recommend that, wherever possible, psychiatrists should spend at least one year abroad, preferably in the country against which they are most prejudiced. It is surprising how in time the other fellow comes to resemble the face in the shaving mirror.

The next job in the gift of the college that came my way was one I enjoyed even more, for the very good reason that I felt better equipped in terms of temperament and basic interests to cope with it: in 1975 I succeeded Denis Leigh as honorary librarian. The college had just then moved from its cramped and wholly inappropriate quarters in Chandos House, Queen Anne Street, W1 to 17 Belgrave Square, SW1, a post-Regency mansion in what must be one of the most elegant districts in all London. Now, for the very first time, the college, or any of its precursors for that matter, had a home to call its own. What is more, it could also, for the first time, have a library which could function as a living organism rather than as an inanimate collection of books.

But the library when I took it over consisted of more than 5000 books and ephemera languishing in a host of crates in the cellars, exposed to damp and the risk of flood. And there they were doomed to remain until such time as a number of formidable obstacles could be overcome. In the first place, stress engineers deemed the floor of the beautiful room earmarked for the library to be too weak to support the dead weight of the books and the paraphernalia that went with them. It would have to be strengthened. To do so meant that the parquet floor would have to be physically lifted, steel girders inserted, and the floor relaid. This done, it became evident that the shelving and bookcases brought from Chandos House were hopelessly inadequate and new ones would have to be designed and built. Lastly, new furniture, curtains, and carpets had to be selected – all within the constraints of a limited budget. It all took endless time and an infinity of patience: but we got there in the end. I say "we" advisedly because without the help of our first professional librarian, Susan Floate, the end result could never have been accomplished.

Once the library was in situ I allowed myself the luxury of a modicum of self-congratulation. It was singularly gratifying to have witnessed, and to have made a contribution towards, the culmination of an evolutionary process which began late last century. The nucleus of this treasure house of knowledge, I reflected, had been a collection of books sufficient in number only to fill a single, not too large, bookcase borrowed by the Medico-Psychological Association from its host when it rented accommodation on a part-time basis from the London Medical Society at 11 Chandos Street, W1.

There was for me the added, almost sensual, pleasure the bibliophile feels when handling old books. To this was added the thrill of knowing that most of our vintage volumes had belonged to, and bore the signatures of, some of our most illustrious predecessors, men who have become part and parcel of psychiatry's folklore. Of particular importance in this context are the many books that had belonged to Dr Daniel Hack Tuke, the great-grandson of the founder of the York Retreat. His widow had given the collection to the Medico-Psychological Association after his death in 1895.

Finally, for those with a trace of commercialism in their veins, it was the prerogative of the honorary librarian to indulge in a little wheeling and dealing with a small but increasing number of booksellers specialising in old and antiquarian books of psychiatric interest. Sometimes it was a question of a straight swap of some item(s) from our stock surplus to our needs for an item which we badly needed. Sometimes the difference in price on either side had to be made up in cash.

One deal that caused me more angst than all the others put together concerned the purchase of an exceedingly rare book which I felt we must have, even if it stretched our financial resources to the limit. This was *A Treatise of Melancholy by T[imothy] Bright, Doctor of Physicke, Imprinted at London by John V. Vindel, 1586.* This treatise, the first by an English physician concerned with mental illness, was the forerunner of Robert Burton's much more famous *Anatomy of Melancholy*, published in 1621. But what makes Bright's treatise additionally attractive is the well founded belief that Shakespeare used it as a source book. There are in our excellently preserved copy a number of faded, but still legible marginal notes written in the elegant script of the time. Could they have been written by the Bard himself? I am not sufficient of a scholar to know, and, what is more, I don't propose to submit them to the scrutiny of someone who is. I would rather that my fantasies remained intact, thank you very much.

In 1985, having served 10 years, I retired from the librarianship, not because I wanted to, but because by statute I had to. My links with the college today are rather more tenuous. I have assumed or have had thrust upon me, not very unwillingly, the role of historiographer and in 1987 published a thumbnail history of the college.[1] A further link is through the *British Journal of Psychiatry* of which I am an assistant editor. I have the mournful job of editing the obituary column, as well as reviewing books and writing the occasional article of a non-technical sort – jobs all designed to keep the remaining cortical cells ticking over, and the ink flowing fairly freely in my pen.

1 Rollin H R. *The Royal College of Psychiatrists.* London: Royal College of Psychiatrists, 1987.

# 17 History of medicine

Any feeling I may have for history in its broadest context I owe to my father, whose interest, although wide-ranging, had a distinct radical political bias. At school I enjoyed history, although it was then taught as a narrative, an exciting story concerned primarily with the struggle for power, a struggle which I came to appreciate very much later was the embodiment of man's innate aggressiveness and potential for violence.

In retrospect, however, I am much more indebted to novelists than to schoolmasters for any appreciation I may have of the political and socioeconomic concomitants of the historical narrative. Charles Dickens, for example, whose works I devoured, painted a far more vivid picture of urban life in Victorian England than I have ever gleaned from history books. The same can be said for his exact contemporary, Mrs Gaskell, who in her novels enters into the very homes and hearts of the suffering poor of Manchester at the time of the Industrial Revolution. She describes with much poignancy the mental disintegration caused by the widespread addiction to alcohol and opium as well as the physical devastation of the then commonplace diseases, cholera and typhus. Analogously, I learnt more about the catastrophic social effects of the great depression in America in the 1930s from John Steinbeck's *The Grapes of Wrath* than I have from any other source.

I was always aware in a somewhat vague and woolly way that there was much to be learnt from history apart from its expressly narrative content, and yet I had virtually no awareness that the same lessons could be learnt from the history of medicine. Had I stopped to think for a moment I would have realised long ago that the history of man is clearly reflected in the history of medicine, or vice versa. In both it is not difficult to trace the same see-saw pattern, the same bold upswing of hope and aspiration to be followed by the downswing of failure and despair. And yet in both, despite heart-breaking reverses, the determination of the human spirit to continue the struggle upwards towards scientific truth and social justice is clearly etched. Nowhere, as I came to learn after I wandered into psychiatry, is this better exemplified than in the history of society's changing attitude to the most underprivileged section of the community – the mentally disordered. For much of this enlightenment I owe undying thanks to Kenneth Bryn Thomas who was my friend and mentor for so many years.

Our initial meeting was, like so many important happenings in my life, entirely fortuitous – an accident of war. In 1941 I was posted to RAF Bridgnorth where Bryn was already established as a specialist anaesthetist. We were immediately en rapport, largely because of the community of our interests, and from then on until his untimely death at the age of 62, in September 1978, we remained the best of good companions.

Bryn was one of the most cultivated men it has ever been my pleasure to know. Not only was he widely read but he was an astute collector of books and medical artefacts, particularly those concerned with the history of anaesthesia: the major part of the collection is now in the possession of the Association of Anaesthetists of Great Britain and Ireland. Above all, he was a medical historian of international repute. Furthermore, it is no idle boast to claim him as one of the world's foremost authorities on the history of anaesthesia. His two major works, namely, *Curare: its History and Usage*, published in 1964, and *The Development of Anaesthetic Apparatus*, published in 1975, were instantly recognised as classics. He was indefatigable in his efforts to promote the study of the history of medicine and to this end he played an important role in every major learned society concerned with the subject. Thus, his service to the section of the history of medicine of the Royal Society of Medicine is probably unparalleled. In 1957 he was elected to the council of the section; from 1959 to 1966 he served as its secretary and, finally, from 1970 to 1972 he was president – in all, 15 years of devoted service. Another of his great loves was the Osler Club of London of which he was deservedly elected president in 1969. It was Bryn's encouragement which led me to seek election to both these societies, and the peaks of my own career as a medical historian were reached when I was elected a vice-president and in 1989 president-elect of the former, and president of the latter from 1974 to 1976.

No portrait, no matter how sketchy, of this handsome, urbane, and generous polymath would be complete without a mention of his brilliance as a teacher. Not only did he have a profound knowledge of his subject, but he had that other vital attribute of a good teacher: he was a superb talker. I have listened to him talk for countless hours in his own home, when sailing with him in his boat on the Thames, or as we walked for miles through the Berkshire countryside – for Bryn, despite his urbanity, was at heart a countryman; and he was, incidentally, the only man I have ever known who could smell a fox.

There was one particularly memorable interlude. Together we attended a meeting of the Harveian Society in Padua in June 1963 and decided to follow the exact route taken by William Harvey centuries before – with this difference, however: he had walked from the Channel port to Padua, a pretty formidable undertaking in itself. We drove.

If further endorsement of Bryn's talents were needed, I have only to turn to my wife, Maria, herself an anaesthetist, who never tires of singing his praises as a teacher in the history of anaesthetics. He never gave a lecture, she says: he gave a performance, and a superb one at that.

My debt to Bryn Thomas as a source of inspiration and encouragement in my study of the history of medicine in general is matched by my debt to Richard Hunter and his mother, Ida Macalpine, in relation to the history of psychiatry in particular. I knew them both well, although not with the same intimacy, or for the same length of time as I knew Bryn. Their deaths within seven years of each other left a yawning gap in the ranks of British medical historians, a gap which, because of the uniqueness of the combination, can never be filled. On 6 May 1982 the Richard Hunter Memorial Collection of Friern Archives was opened at Friern Hospital, New Southgate, London, and I was honoured to be asked to give the dedicatory address. A paper based on the address was published in the *Cambridge Review* in 1983.[1]

1 Rollin H R. Richard Hunter, MD (1923–1981) *Cambridge Review* 1987; Feb: 71–4.

# 18 Therapeutic use of music in a mental hospital

Musick is a roaring-meg against melancholy, to rear and revive the languishing soul: affecting not only the ears, but the very arteries, the vital and animal spirits, it erects the mind and makes it nimble. – ROBERT BURTON (1577–1640), *Anatomy of Melancholy*.

The theories designed to explain how music exercises its powers are many, and I do not propose to add to them. Suffice it to say, however, that a primary disturbance in so much mental illness is in the emotions. Schizophrenics, for example, who make up such a large proportion of a mental hospital population, suffer particularly in this respect. A characteristic of the disease, emotional flattening or an inability to respond appropriately in terms of feeling to a given situation, is often manifest. Again, among victims of affective disorders there is a morbid distortion of emotions ranging from elation or pathological happiness on the one hand, to melancholia or pathological unhappiness on the other. Indeed, one would be hard put to discover any form of mental illness, psychotic or neurotic, in which the emotions are not symptomatically involved. Music, it was felt, therefore, could be employed as a means whereby these emotional upsets could be attacked, either by stimulation or sedation, and the fundamental disease progress thereby mitigated. Let it be emphasised, however, that at no time was it considered possible that music could replace established methods of treatment such as electroconvulsive therapy, psychotherapy, or chemical agents. From the beginning it was always considered that music, in the light of our present knowledge at any rate, could be rated as only an ancillary form of treatment, or perhaps as a catalyst, facilitating other therapeutic procedures. Our sights were deliberately kept low. Music therapy must still be regarded as an experimental project and modesty in its immediate aims in this, as in any other experiment, is not necessarily a handicap.

When we began at Horton Hospital, Epsom, in 1955, there were no preconceived notions as to what the precise objectives should be or how the project with the aid of one music therapist employed for one day a week should be put into operation. (I should add here that there was then a "music appreciation programme" in existence attended by all who cared to go, but it was felt that what must be done now should be more specific and individual.) There was no equipment except an antique piano salvaged from a ward and restored to its inferior best, and an electric gramophone. Initially, the only accommodation available was the main hall, built in the grand Victorian manner and large enough to house a fleet of mammoth aircraft, but with acoustics which had to be heard – or not heard – to be believed. But a start was made. To begin with, we selected a group of men patients who had had musical tuition either as professionals or as amateurs. It was felt on prima facie grounds that to reawaken an interest in an activity which at one time must have given deep satisfaction ought to be of therapeutic value. No attention was paid to the mental disease from which the patients suffered or the phase of their illness. As by far the largest single clinical group in any mental hospital is that of schizophrenics, it is not surprising that of the nine patients who comprised the first group, eight were schizophrenics and one a manic depressive. Of the nine, one had been a professional pianist of some standing; one had been a student at an academy of music at the time of his breakdown; another had been an amateur violinist of above average ability, and the rest had been pianists of widely differing levels of achievement.

The schedule at first was simple. After the patients assembled, gramophone records – initially selected by the therapist but later selected by the patients themselves – were played. Then the therapist played piano solos, mainly, as the programme got under way, by request. Finally, each patient in turn was urged to play something – anything – at the piano. It must be remembered that not one of the patients had touched an instrument since admission to the hospital, which was for periods varying from several weeks to 20 years. The standard of performance, therefore, varied enormously from passing fair to excruciatingly bad. But virtuosity was not the objective: what was asked for and what was obtained, with a minimum or a maximum degree of cajolery and encouragement, was participation. It was heartening in those early days to see retarded and/or deteriorated patients scramble, some way at any rate, out of their psychosis and communicate by means of the music they played with their fellow men. That the communication was received was manifest in the applause of the rest of the patients for the performance, no matter how inferior it was. A group was formed spontaneously from individuals who by virtue of their mental illness tended to be solitary and asocial. It was the creation of this group – that is, an association of people with a common purpose and a common language, in this case music – which paved the way to future endeavours. Lest the one and only violinist be forgotten let it be said that he had his fiddle sent from home and that his contributions as a soloist, duettist, or in various small ensembles were greatly appreciated.

Some time later, equivalent groups of women patients, selected by the same criteria, were formed and with a success no less than with the male groups. By early 1956 more than 30 patients had been included who had specifically asked to be so, or whose relatives had requested their inclusion. From these heterogeneous groups, a few patients, men and women, had crystallised out as being especially gifted, musically speaking, and to these individual tuition was given.

In the summer of 1956 an important milestone was reached: a superb Steinway grand piano was acquired by an unusual example of Anglo-American cooperation. The long and benevolent arm of Madame Yolanda Mero-Irion, executive director of the Hospitalized Veterans Service of the Musicians Emergency Fund, Inc, in America, reached across the Atlantic and interceded on our behalf with Messrs Steinway of London, so that the instrument was made available at a very special price, which was paid by the Horton management committee. This was not only a symbol of success in that the committee was sufficiently impressed with the experiment in music therapy to give its blessing in such a tangible form, but also as a boost to the morale of patients and staff alike. To play this magnificent instrument in preference to the antique model already described became a privilege, so that there was competition between patients to be allowed to do so, either during music therapy sessions or during practice sessions which had by now been drawn up.

By now the number of patients receiving music therapy had steadily increased and, as a further group activity, a women's choir had been formed. The standard of playing of the few patients for whom time had been found to give individual instruction had improved inordinately. Indeed, it was felt that the time was now ripe for concerts to be given by the patients for the patients. These were started in the spring of 1956. The programmes were ambitious, and, considering the material with which the music therapist had to work, the fact that they were performed at all, at any level, was in itself an achievement. Some of the performances were extremely good. Perfection was not aimed at and certainly not attained; but what was achieved was a psychological triumph for performers and audience alike. The frequent rehearsals had welded the performers into a large group, with the same group and individual tensions and anxieties which normal musical groups undergo in similar circumstances. The fillip to their egos once they had done their bit was all too obvious. They glowed with pride as they took their bows and again when they received their little gifts as tokens of appreciation of their efforts. Temporarily, at any rate, they had fulfilled man's fundamental need – to be needed. The mentally ill, admitted perforce to a mental hospital, are for the length of their stay failures. They have failed their social group, their families, and particularly themselves. What better index of hope for the future could there be than to stand in the limelight, in both the literal and metaphorical sense, to receive the plaudits of their fellows? For the audience, composed of over 300 patients, shared in the success of the concerts and reflected glory of the performers, and in so doing they too became part of the group – the music therapy group – in just the same way as a school, a university, or a whole town can project themselves into, and identify themselves with, the triumph of their team. As further evidence of this phenomenon it should be mentioned that these patients' concerts occasioned much more discussion for a much longer time than any given by outside artists, no matter how eminent.

Having established these musically-orientated groups, we felt that the net could be cast wider and experimental groups started with patients to whom music, or rather rhythm, might appeal at a more primitive level. To this end, in March 1957, percussion bands were formed with, as the stock of instruments gradually increased, drums, tambourines, triangles, cymbals, bells, maracas, tambours, chime bars, trumpets, and "nightingales". The criterion for inclusion in these groups was that no other form of treatment had been able to hold the patient's interest. Clinically, therefore, they constituted the least hopeful element in the hospital. The technique was quite simple: the piano was played with a forceful rhythm, usually incidentally by another patient, while the patients in the group were encouraged by members of the staff to shake or beat the percussion instruments which had been handed to them. These instruments require no musical skill whatever; all that is needed is to determine and maintain the rhythm of the piano. The result is not nearly as cacophonous as might be expected in spite of, or because of, the limitations in tonal range. In fact, with a percussion band going full blast, and this is the desired result, the effect can be very stirring. The regressed schizophrenics who made up most of these groups are by the nature of their psychosis withdrawn, apathetic, and anergic, so that spontaneous participation was not expected or achieved. However, with coaxing and encouragement, most of the patients were induced to play their part, or their instrument, at first feebly, but later with growing gusto. The success of the venture could indeed be measured quite simply by the volume of sound which emerges from the group, and in this respect a decibel recording instrument is not needed: an arbitrary assessment can be made from the distance from the music room before the group can be heard – or from the volume of complaint from neighbouring departments or offices. There can be no doubt that these percussion groups succeeded within the limited objective set for them. It is most reassuring to see these lost, preoccupied beings become, for the moment at any rate, animated and "have a go" with whatever instrument they happen to wield.

In July 1957, a second important milestone was reached: the acquisition of a music room. In keeping with other assembly halls at Horton the chapel is of giant proportions, far too large for the spiritual needs of the community, patients, and staff. With the kind cooperation of the management committee and the ecclesiastical authorities, permission was obtained to annex roughly a quarter of the chapel as a music room and concert hall. The conversion was duly completed and opened on 7 December 1961 by the Countess of Harewood, after whom the hall was named.

The acquisition of a home of its own gave the music therapy project a decided fillip. New experimental schemes were set in motion and yet another group, a recorder group with mouth organ and/or banjo and autoharp plus a percussion section accompanied at the piano by a patient, was formed and proved a great favourite. Indeed, so great were the patients' demands for practice time, either for individual patients or small ensembles, at times other than the official music therapy sessions, that later a second music room was fashioned from a disused general bathroom, and two reasonable upright pianos housed there.

A complicated organism such as a mental hospital is never static. The turnover at Horton was substantially more than 1000 patients a year. Among them were individuals who because of their special talents could be incorporated into the music therapy programme, which has always been kept sufficiently elastic to allow for considerable modifications. For example, a male patient of 32 under treatment for obsessive-compulsive neurosis had had a professional training as a composer and conductor. He not only organised and trained a mixed chorus – mixed in terms of sex and clinical conditions – to a laudable degree of efficiency, but wrote arrangements of popular songs to suit his unorthodox group in addition to composing works of his own for it.

It would be pertinent to add a note concerning the attitude of the nursing staff to the project. To begin with there was an understandable scepticism, which gave way as the scheme got under way, and particularly after the most successful patients' concerts already referred to, to growing enthusiasm and increasing cooperation. There were then up to eight members of the nursing staff, men and women, present during the sessions, and their help was particularly valuable with the percussion groups where so much encouragement and coaxing is needed to ensure the patients' participation in the activity. It is noteworthy, too, that two men recruits to the nursing staff, both of whom had had musical training, came to Horton because of its music therapy programme. Their help in carrying on the work, particularly with the ensembles, in the absence of the music therapist was most valuable. Furthermore, the interest and cooperation of the occupational therapy department was wholehearted, and attendance at the groups was considered as an integral part of the training of student occupational therapists at the hospital. As a result of the marriage between the occupational therapy and music therapy departments percussion band sessions were held as a regular feature of the former's programme for its chronic patients and were directed by one of its own staff.

One of the most satisfactory and satisfying developments in the use of music, and one on which increasing emphasis was placed, was in the geriatric wards. Inherent in the problem of treating the aged, no matter what the individual psychopathology may be, is how to combat boredom. To this end music was used in a variety of ways. At the suggestion of the nursing staff "keep fit" classes were held, admittedly of a very simple kind. In these, movement and relaxation to the accompaniment of gramophone records were encouraged, and then, under the aegis of the music therapist, a percussion band was formed which went from strength to strength, or rather from volume to volume. Perhaps the most popular of all the activities was the weekly concert-cum-dance. In this session, live music was provided by members of the regular music therapy classes to a mixed group of 60 to 70 old people who foregathered in a large women's ward. The afternoon's programme consisted of musical items provided by individuals and groups, all designed so that the old people could join in choruses, add their quota of sound with percussion instruments which were handed round, or merely clap their hands or stamp their feet to the rhythm. After a communal tea an impromptu dance was held during which the Darbys and the Joans took the floor either spontaneously or with encouragement from the staff. Here again, what was asked for and obtained was participation of a surprising degree. That the entertainment was enjoyed was manifest in the party spirit which abounded, the applause for the entertainers and the degree to which both sexes "dressed up" for the occasion.

In this account of the growth and development of music therapy in Horton hospital I have made no attempt to assess the improvement, either individually or collectively, which resulted. This is because years of experience have strengthened my belief that music is not, and is never likely to be, a primary form of treatment in mental illness. However, as an ancillary, or, perhaps, catalytic form of treatment I have no doubt that music plays its part, and an important part at that.

# 19 Literary excursions

"Such and so various are the tastes of men", or, if you prefer, "one man's meat is another man's poison". These are examples of an infinite number of axioms or proverbs to be trotted out in order to illustrate the undeniable fact that no two men are the same in their likes or dislikes or, to lapse into the modern idiom, in what turns them on or turns them off. And what applies to neckties, meat, music, lingerie, or drink applies equally to literature.

What those of my readers who have borne with me thus far will know is that since childhood I have both read voraciously and indulged a consuming passion for the theatre. As a result the literary and dramatic input has been very substantial indeed. At the same time, particularly in the past 40 years or so, it has been my exceeding good fortune to have achieved a considerable output of articles on medical, or more precisely, psychiatric matters. In addition I have been the author of papers, which failing all else, I have chosen to grace with the somewhat grandiose term "literary". But here again I cannot escape my one and only discipline, and therefore my literary excursions are perforce wedded to what I know best. Having said this, I am faced with the problem of what examples of the genre I can include and what I can leave out.

Having no knowledge of the literary tastes of my readers, which, as I have already indicated, must be as various as the colours of a punk's hairdo, I am indulging in the conceit of being my own arbiter.

I make no apology for the essays I have chosen because they reflect my devotion to some of my particular literary heroes, to wit, Shakespeare, Lord Byron, George Bernard Shaw, and James Joyce.

# HAMLET: PSYCHIATRY'S ENIGMA VARIATIONS

The preoccupation with Shakespeare of psychiatrists, or at any rate, writers adopting a psychiatric approach, dates as far as I can determine from 1780, when Henry Mackenzie kicks off with his "Criticism on the Character and Tragedy of Hamlet" in the *Mirror*, published in Edinburgh. The ball then lands in touch and stays there for some 40 years until Francis Willis re-starts play with "A Treatise on Mental Derangement", his Gulstonian lecture in 1822 in which he analyses Lady Macbeth, Lear, Ophelia, Hamlet, and Edgar. From then on the pace not only quickens but becomes an international free-for-all, and there is no sign as yet that the final whistle will ever be blown. An excellent and breezy commentary on this academic game is contained in Dr André Adnès's book *Shakespeare et la Pathologie Mentale*, published in 1935, which appends a bibliography with no fewer than 153 references.[1] Eighty-two of these are in English, using the term generically to include American writings; 44 are in German, 18 in French, six in Italian, and one each in Russian, Dutch, and Polish. The list is, of course, incomplete and does not, for example, include more recent contributions by Dr E S Stern, Dr W I D Scott, and Professor Russell Davis.

It is of interest to highlight those characters in Shakespeare which have come under psychiatric scrutiny. Using Dr Adnès's references only, Hamlet tops the First Division easily with 45 points, Lear comes second with 10 points, then Ophelia seven, Macbeth six, Lady Macbeth and Othello two each. Timon of Athens and Jaques share the bottom of the Third Division with my favourite character, that rascally pickpurse of Gadshill, Falstaff, with one point each.

I wonder, incidentally, if it is any compensation for my fat friend and fellow-toper to know that although he may have been scurrilously forgotten by his erstwhile friend, Prince Henry, with his, "I know thee not, old man", he will now be remembered for all time in the *Psychoanalytic Quarterly* of 1933 in a paper by Dr F Alexander.

To survey all the relevant psychiatric literature on the

characters in Shakespeare would be impossible. I propose, therefore, to confine myself to the principal target, Hamlet, although anything approaching a full-scale commentary on the commentaries is equally impossible.

With few exceptions, notably Henry Maudsley, all the psychiatric commentators assume that Hamlet, poor fellow, is mentally ill. Professor Edward Dowden, a distinguished Victorian professor of English literature in the University of Dublin, alleges: "The doctors of the insane have been studious of the state of Hamlet's mind – Doctors Ray, Kellog, Conolly, Maudsley, Bucknill. They are unanimous in wishing to put Hamlet under judicious medical treatment."[2]

Maudsley, in the preface to his elegant essay "Shakespeare: Testimonied in his own Bringingsforth" quotes Dowden's allegation in order to refute it and is at pains to point out that, ". . . the main motive of my Essay was to show that there was not the least ground to suppose that Hamlet was mad or meant by Shakespeare to be thought mad."[3]

Chateaubriand in his "Essai sur la littérature anglaise" (1836) takes a diametrically opposite view and insists that not only is Hamlet himself as mad as a hatter, but that Elsinore is itself a veritable madhouse or a "Bedlam royal où tout le monde est insensé et criminel, où la démence simulée se joint à la démence vraie, òu le fou contrefait le fou, où les morts eux-mêmes fournissent à la scène la tête d'un fou."

Between these two, Maudsley and Chateaubriand, the commentators – all of whom, like Hamlet "know not seems" but are quite categorical in their opinions – attach their diagnostic labels so that in the end he emerges with more diagnoses than Caesar had wounds. "Hamlet, the classical malingerer" (R Alexander, 1929); "Hamlet mélancolie simple, ennui de la vie et folie simulée" (A Brierre de Boismont, 1868); "On the feyned madness of Hamlet" (*Blackwood's Edinburgh Magazine*, 1839); "Hamlet als Neurastheniker" (H Haacke, 1896); "Hamlet – The Manic Depressive" (W I D Scott, 1962); "Three Ganser States and Hamlet" (E S Stern, 1941). Professor Russell Davis (*Lancet*, 1964) is somewhat more cautious and non-committal when he says, "It would be meaningless and unprofitable to argue, for instance, whether

Hamlet or Ophelia suffered from Schizophrenia, but it would be unobjectionable if they were both included in a series of psychoses with an onset after puberty, and before the 25th birthday."[4]

The psychopathological interpretations of Hamlet's alleged mental illness are, as might be expected, as various as its diagnoses. In all fairness to the psychoanalytic interpreters it should be pointed out that there is more than a modicum of consistency among them in that they tend to incriminate the Oedipus complex as the root cause of Hamlet's enigmatic derangement.

So the collective opinions of Hamlet's psychiatrists form a veritable bran-tub from which any diagnosis in the psychiatric calendar can be picked. It could be fairly said, therefore, that Hamlet was not only:

> The expectancy and rose of the fair state,
> The glass of fashion, and the mould of form,

but also that he carried on his back most of the textbooks on psychiatry ever written.

How comes it that there can be such divergent opinions as to the nature of Hamlet's mental illness, if indeed he suffered from one at all?

One possible explanation is the widely differing deductions drawn from the data provided by the text. I would like to explore this possibility by comparing the work of two medical writers chosen not only because their views are divergent, but because they express themselves concisely and convincingly within their own terms of reference. The writers are both English and roughly contemporaneous and their use of medical and psychiatric terms should be, therefore, strictly comparable. Furthermore, most conveniently for me, they use identical passages, and at times, identical lines in the text to point their different arguments.

The two writers I refer to are Dr W I D Scott and his chapter "Hamlet – The Manic Depressive" in a book entitled *Shakespeare's Melancholics*, published in 1962,[5] and Dr E S Stern and his "Three Ganser States and Hamlet", published in

1942.[6] Dr Stern, incidentally, defines the Ganser state as occurring in people who, although mentally deranged, not realising this, wish to appear so. He points to one particular characteristic, namely, that of giving "crooked answers" to questions.

To begin with, in order to substantiate their different clinical theses it is essential for the two writers to prove to their own satisfaction whether Hamlet was or was not hallucinated. To arrive at a positive conclusion in this respect Stern uses the scene (Act III, iv) between Hamlet and his mother, the Queen, when the Ghost of his father appears to him alone and speaks to him alone. The Queen, witnessing Hamlet's sudden preoccupation says:

> Alas how is't with you,
> That you do bend your eye on vacancy
> And with the incorporal air do hold discourse?

Scott, on the other hand, concludes differently, and explains the appearance of the Ghost to Hamlet and the verbal interchange between them in the same scene by saying, "It is a dramatic convention that a character may be heard clearly by the audience and by only one other person on the stage." He goes on further ". . . if it is accepted that Hamlet is hallucinated, he cannot be suffering from simple depressive illness. Hallucinations are characteristic of toxic brain conditions and particularly of schizophrenia: they never appear in the manic-depressive psychosis" – the diagnosis Scott supports.[5]

The problem of why and when Hamlet feigned insanity and its significance in the drama is of great importance, and both writers approach and assess it differently.

In Act I, v Hamlet makes clear his intention:

> How strange or odd so e'er I bear myself,
> As I perchance hereafter shall think meet
> To put an antic disposition on.

Stern maintains that he decides to feign insanity because he has no insight into his underlying psychosis. Scott, however, states, "It is difficult to understand what Hamlet had to gain by feigning insanity," and goes on, "The assumed insanity is put on mainly for the benefit of Polonius, whose wagging tongue can be relied on to spread the news throughout the Court."[5]

Again, in Act II, i, Ophelia describes to her father, Polonius, her terrifying experience with Hamlet in her chamber:

> My Lord, as I was sewing in my closet,
> Lord Hamlet, with his doublet all unbrac'd,
> No hat upon his head; his stockings foul'd,
> Ungarter'd, and down-gyvved to his ankle;
> Pale as his shirt; his knees knocking each other;
> And with a look so piteous in purport
> As if he had been loosed out of hell
> To speak of horrors, he comes before me.

Stern says, "This simulation is first seen when he [Hamlet] appears all dishevelled before Ophelia."[6] But Scott, referring to the same lines as Stern quoted above, maintains that "This is clearly real and not assumed distraction."[5] He indeed, dates the onset of Hamlet's "antic disposition" from the doggerel, the nonsensical verse written to Ophelia:

> Doubt thou the stars are fire;
> Doubt that the sun doth move;
> Doubt truth to be a liar;
> But never doubt I love.

Finally, in Act III, i, in that poignant scene between Hamlet and Ophelia when she returns his gifts and he, in turn, attempts to cast her off giving his own unworthiness as his excuse:

Get thee to a nunnery: why wouldst thou be a breeder of sinners? I am myself indifferent honest; but yet I could accuse me of such things that it were better my mother had not borne me. I am very proud, revengeful, ambitious; with more offences at my beck than I have thoughts to put them in, imagination to give them shape, or time to act them in. What should such fellows as I do crawling between heaven and earth? We are arrant knaves, all; believe none of us. Go thy ways to a nunnery.

Stern says, referring to Hamlet's bewildering behaviour

158

towards the young ingenuous girl: "He also *pretends* to be insane with her."[6] Scott, on the other hand, quoting extensively from the same scene, explains, "The enumeration of his [Hamlet's] faults is characteristic of the sense of unworthiness of the true melancholic, *and I regard it as absolutely sincere.*"[5]

Which, then, of these learned opinions is the correct one if, indeed, either is? For myself I would not wager one Barbary horse, let alone six. But for those of you who would like a flutter may I make confusion worse confounded and add this piece of last-minute inside information from that eminent scholar, Professor G Wilson Knight? Claudius, the King, who, as far as I am aware, is always regarded as "incestuous, murderous, damned Dane", was presented by Professor Knight in the BBC programme *Lift up your Hearts*, on 20 April 1964, as a kindly and gentle man and was offered to his listeners as an example of Christian rectitude!

The other possible explanation for the diversity of psychiatric opinion as to the existence of, or the nature of, the mental illness in Hamlet or any other Shakespearean character lies in the question: to what extent are these wholly or predominantly fictitious people susceptible to psychiatric examination? In this respect it is as well to remember that even in the history plays there is absolutely no guarantee that the portraits painted by Shakespeare have any real historical validity. Recent researches, for example, have considerably rehabilitated the character of Richard III who, nevertheless, will continue to live in our memory through Shakespeare as a black-hearted, hunchbacked, villain. What purpose, then, is served by translating Hamlet, or Richard, or any other of the long gallery of characters created by Shakespeare for the stage, which is the only place they really come to life, to the psychiatrist's consulting room, or the analyst's couch?

Shakespeare was a highly professional playwright, a professional actor and an ardent playgoer. He of all people knew his theatre in the literal and metaphorical sense, in the round. For him the play's the thing, and the basis of the play the plot. He was not a great inventor of plots, but he borrowed the best available, and in order to develop them fully he was prepared to subordinate the characters to their development. In other words, to suit the purposes of his plots, the characters in them could be stretched to the limits of credibility and even beyond. But because they may be incredible it does not mean that they are mad as judged by ordinary clinical psychiatric standards.

To turn again to Hamlet, it seems clear that Shakespeare borrowed the plot from the *Histoires Tragiques* of François de Belleforest (published in Paris in 1570) who adapted it from a much earlier Danish source. It is a horrific tale calculated to chill the blood, and every hair-raising ingredient is thrown into the brew, including regicide, fratricide, incest, and feigned madness. In all essential details Shakespeare's play is true to its original source. In the realisation of this fantastic human or inhuman maelstrom it is not surprising that the central figure, Hamlet, turns out himself to be fantastic. He is not, therefore, and in my opinion, never was intended to be the representation of any real person. If Hamlet has any consistency at all it is only with himself. If this is so then every diagnostic label tagged onto him may be right, or may be wrong. He may be suffering from any or all of the neuroses, or any or all of the psychoses attributed to him. Or he may have none of these things. The more one attempts to peel off the skins of the onion to see what lies within, the more persistently does Hamlet remain the Prince of Denmark.

If Shakespeare has anything further to contribute to psychiatry it is this: let there be no more pedagogic psychiatric excursions into the mental states of fictitious figures in a fictitious world. Psychiatry has enough on its plate if it is to put its own house in order and if it is to make its contribution to the solution of the problems of real people in a real world.

1 Adnès A. *Shakespeare et la pathologie mentale*. Paris: Librairie Maloine, 1935.
2 Dowden E. *Shakespeare: his mind and art*. London: Kegan Paul, Trench, Trubner, 1901.
3 Maudsley H. *Shakespeare: "testimonied in his own bringingsforth"*. London: John Bale, Sons & Danielsson, 1905.
4 Davis R D. Family processes in mental illness. *Lancet* 1964; i: 733.
5 Scott W I D. Hamlet—the manic depressive. In: *Shakespeare's melancholics*. London: Mills and Boon, 1962.
6 Stern E S. Three Ganser states and Hamlet. *J Mental Science* 1942; 88:

# CHILDE HAROLD: FATHER TO LORD BYRON?

If Byron had not existed, it would have been impossible to invent him: to create a character in fiction to match Byron would be to stretch credulity to absurdity. And yet behind the charisma, the brouhaha, and the myth there lurks a man, a very extraordinary man, a genius maybe, but a man nevertheless, whose character, image, personality, or what-have-you is compounded, as in lesser mortals, from elements derived from his heredity and his environment; from his nature and his nurture.

The study of personality is my business: the study of Byron a major interest. I have no illusions about the task I have set myself, but I draw comfort from the fact that it is just because Byron was himself so very extraordinary that whatever pathology there may be either in his heredity or in his environment, or both, would be gross and, therefore, easily demonstrable. Furthermore, fortunately for me, there is available a wealth of unimpeachable biographical, autobiographical, and other documentary evidence covering his brief life. Even so, I am all too aware of the traps for the unwary in the retrospective psychiatric interpretation of such evidence. So I will tread very softly lest I tread on the corns, if not the dreams, of Byron's idolators.

What of Byron's heredity? There is evidence enough that there was rot in more than a few branches of his family tree. Nicknames, particularly pejorative ones, are usually well deserved. It was not without significance that so many of Byron's male antecedents bore such names. "The Wicked Lord", from whom Byron inherited his title and estates, was a great-uncle. He was foul-tempered, irascible, and spiteful to a degree. Such was his reputation and his behaviour that Horace Walpole after once meeting him was heard to remark, "the present Lord Byron is a madman." Byron's grandfather, a feckless vice-admiral, earned for himself the name tag "Foul-weather Jack". Captain John Byron, the poet's father, could today have been easily classified as a psychopath. Because of his violent temper and financial irresponsibility he became known as "Mad Jack". True to type, he scandalised society by his elopement with the wife of Lord Carmarthen, and it was said that he was responsible for her death in 1784 shortly after the birth of Augusta, Byron's half-sister. Captain Byron's grief, if indeed he was capable of any such sentiment, was short-lived. He set his cap at Miss Gordon of Gight, who was to be the poet's mother, attracted not by her beauty or charm, which she had in very short measure, but by her one and only asset – a not inconsiderable fortune. The marriage was predictably a disaster. He died apparently by his own hand in 1791 having squandered his wife's fortune and subjected her to every form of physical and social degradation.

Byron's antecedents on the female side are marginally less unfortunate, but bad enough in all conscience. His mother was a Gordon descended from a long line of well born brigands, notorious for their violence and impulsiveness – characteristics she herself inherited in plenty.

From an hereditary standpoint, therefore, it seems clear that whatever other assets may have come his way stability and equanimity were not likely to be counted among them. Even so, it has been shown that, given the right environmental circumstances, the hereditary mark of Cain can be counter-balanced. But Byron was as miserably unlucky in his nurture, particularly in his earliest formative period, as he was in his nature.

The "broken home" obtained in Byron's case. "Mad Jack" died when Byron was but 3 years old and he can have had little if any conscious recollection of him. In effect he was an absentee father, who on his rare visits to the matrimonial home succeeded in creating greater chaos in what was already a chaotic atmosphere. To add to the insecurity occasioned by the absence of a corporeal father, Pelion was heaped on Ossa by the creation of a phantom father in whom all evil and wickedness were invested, by the joint efforts of his mother and the two harpies, Agnes and May Gray, her maids. "You little dog. You're a thorough Byron: you are just as bad as your father" is an example of his mother's cruel, irresponsible type of reproof during one of her violent rages. And yet there were times when she became over-solicitous about his welfare, so adding to the uncertainty of her real feelings towards him.

If anything, the mother-son relationship deteriorated as Byron grew older, to a point where his holidays from school became a nightmare. In 1804 he wrote to Augusta, his half-sister and now confidante, "Am I to call this woman mother? Because by nature's law she has authority over me, am I to be trampled upon in this manner? Am I to be goaded with insult, loaded with obloquy? I owe her respect as a son, but I renounce her as a friend. What example does she show me! I hope in God I shall never follow it."

In addition to their role as maids to Mrs Byron, the sisters Agnes and May Gray served as nurses to young Byron. Their influences could have been nothing but malignant. May in particular exemplified hypocritical Calvinism at its worst. She was well versed in the Bible, especially those purple passages to do with the rewards of sin. For the bedtime stories of more fortunate children she substituted hair-raising ghost stories. Mr Hanson, the poet's attorney, wrote to Mrs Byron to "apprize you of the proceedings of your servant Mrs Gray." Byron then aged 10 had told him ". . . that she was perpetually beating him and that his bones sometimes ached from it: that she brought all sorts of Company of the lowest Description into his apartments . . ."

In favourable circumstances schoolmasters may act as father-surrogates, and in this respect young Byron was less fortunate than most. His earliest education was in Scotland, where at that time schools were famed for their physical discomfort and the rigours of their religious instruction – that is, more Sin and Satan. Though recognised as intelligent at Aberdeen Grammar School, he received little encouragement and seems to have been left to his own devices. Later, at Harrow, and for the first time, he came under the influence of someone in authority who was both stern and just. He became the "untamed colt led by the silken cord of Dr Drury", the headmaster. But he was then $13\frac{1}{2}$ and by that time irreparable damage had been done.

No account of Byron's psychopathology would be complete without a mention of his lameness. The precise diagnosis is still disputed, but whatever it may have been he was, from a functional standpoint, only minimally handicapped.

He was, after all, a superb swimmer, an average fencer and boxer, and a competent horseman. But for one as narcissistic as he was to be maimed and imperfect, no matter in what degree, was intolerable. What served to aggravate the trauma a thousandfold was the inhuman treatment he was subjected to ostensibly to correct the deformity, and to add salt to the wound, the jeering and taunting he received – even from his mother. "A lame brat" was the most hurtful of the many epithets she hurled at him.

It is difficult to imagine a more pathological environment than the one the young poet was raised in, an environment indeed that could widen the cracks in his hereditary equipment to a point where what defences he had began to give way and deviant behaviour, neurotic, or even psychotic symptoms were allowed to seep through. Evidence of just this course of events is tragically plentiful.

That Byron, who had known so much fear in infancy, should be plagued in adult life by overt symptoms of pathological anxiety is in no way surprising. He was haunted by insomnia. When he did fall asleep he was tormented by nightmares, from which he would awaken in such a state of terror that he would summon his manservant, Fletcher, to reassure him and calm him down. He gnawed his nails unmercifully; the contrast between them and his otherwise well shaped, well kept hands must have been striking and, to him, painful. In later life he could not be separated from his pistols, which he kept under his pillow at night and on his person during the day. There were times when he had recourse to opiates. In a letter dated 18 March, 1808, he wrote to his friend John Cam Hobhouse, "The Game is almost up, for these last five days I have been confined to my room. Laudanum is my sole support."

His tolerance of frustration was low, with the result that if thwarted he would fly into tempestuous rages, which despite the hopes he expressed in his letter to Augusta were a pretty fair facsimile of those of his unstable mother. He had never in his formative years been inculcated with a sense of loyalty, which might well explain his own disloyalty. A good example is his treatment of his guardian, Lord Carlisle. Originally he intended to pay him a gracious compliment in *English Bards and Scotch Reviewers* with

> On one alone Apollo deigns to smile
> And crowns a new Roscommon in Carlisle

Later in order to satisfy a vicious whim the couplet is altered to read

> No Muse will cheer, with renovating smile,
> The paralytic puling of Carlisle

His cavalier treatment of Lady Caroline Lamb, and indeed his wife, among others he became involved with could also be interpreted in the context of disloyalty, though obviously there were other factors at work. He had never been exposed to altruism, so that throughout his life he remained self-centred, vain, and arrogantly conceited. It could well be that, like his romanticism, his defence of the principle of nationalism was only half sincere. It could be indeed that his active support of the Italians and Greeks in their fight for self-determination was inspired by his ambition to re-live the life of his crusading ancestors rather than an earnest effort to help the oppressed throw off their shackles.

Conceivably Byron's revolt against the earliest form of authority, that of his mother, is echoed in his rebellion against all forms of established authority: the political system, the social systems, the royal house, and, what in the light of his upbringing, he might be expected to accept as the highest authority – God. Thus, politically, he was an advanced Whig. In his first speech in the House of Lords he took up the cause of the "framebreakers" of Nottingham, a defence in point of fact of the wage-earners against the tyranny of the manufacturers. Napoleon, the arch-rebel, was his lifelong hero: he made no secret of his support of Bonaparte even when the Allies had invaded France.

His sympathy lay with the underdog, not only in a socioeconomic sense (for hadn't the hobbling little gamin of Aberdeen been very much the underdog?). He made so bold as to attack the Prince Regent openly in *The Corsair* for his treatment of his daughter, Princess Charlotte, herself the victim of an insufferable parent-child relationship:

> Weep, daughter of a royal line,
> A Sire's disgrace, a realm's decay;
> Ah! happy if each tear of thine
> Could wash a father's fault away!

He leaned heavily towards agnosticism but the perverted Calvinism, the "torments of hell-fire" in which he had been raised, was not easily eradicated. To the end of his days Byron had an acute awareness of sin – and he was a very determined sinner – which he described eloquently as "the nightmare of my own delinquencies". He was, therefore, immoral rather than amoral.

Nevertheless, it is, I believe, in his psychosexual development, or maldevelopment, that the root cause of the Byronic tragedy is to be found. In the psychological sense Byron lacked a father, nor did a father-surrogate materialise in his crucial formative years. Even the phantom father created for him by his mother was an ogre. She herself was ogre-like and responsible for the grimly unhappy relationship with her son. In the absence of precepts, guidelines, and sources of identification normally provided by parents or their surrogates, Byron was left to navigate the hazardous seas of his early psychosexual development without compass or rudder – and was shipwrecked. The ultimate destination, that of full heterosexual development fitting him for a lasting relationship as in marriage, was never reached. He was, in other words, sexually immature and remained so. This is perhaps an explanation of his "polymorphperversity", by which is meant an attempt on his part to find sexual gratification with partners irrespective of their age or sex. There is thus evidence of his indulgence in about the whole spectrum of sexual deviancy from homosexuality to gerontophilia.

In his affairs with women of all social classes, excessive even by the libertine standards of the time, there is more than a suggestion of desperation. In every Don Juan – and ironically Byron showed it to the nth degree – there is a need to pursue women relentlessly in the hope that one at least will afford him sexual gratification. In another letter addressed to his friend Hobhouse in 1808 he says, "I am buried in an abyss of sensuality ... I am at this moment under a course of restoration by Pearson's prescription ... for a debility occasioned by too frequent Connection."

There can be little doubt of Byron's homosexuality, another manifestation of psychosexual immaturity. At Harrow and later at Cambridge he surrounded himself with attractive boys and young men. For example, at Cambridge he had a relationship with a humble chorister, John Edelston, for whom, as he later put it, he had "a violent though pure love and passion". Similarly, he became involved with Nicolo Giraud, a humble Levantine he met in Athens.

His ill fated marriage is proof enough of his unsuitability for a heterosexual relationship of any permanency. His wife, Annabella, was desirable in every respect and eminently suited to be his wife. Yet to have to live with her intimately and permanently was intolerable. It is pertinent to note that it was towards the end of his brief married life that his anxiety neurosis – if that is what his manifold symptoms amounted to – suffered an acute exacerbation. His sanity was called into question. Byron had sufficient insight to state openly that it was his marriage that was nearly driving him out of his senses. It was at this time too that his friends feared lest he should take his life.

It is most significant that the only women in whose company he felt at peace were those who, in fact or fantasy, combined the attributes of a mistress and a mother; someone to whom he could turn for love, comfort, security, and solace when he was troubled and sorely tried – the eternal child-mother relationship.

Fact and fantasy are combined in his relationship with Lady Oxford, a woman almost 20 years his senior, with whom, after escaping from the clutches of Lady Caroline Lamb, he lived in idyllic bliss throughout the autumn of 1812. Fantasy replaces fact, but only just, in his association with Lady Melbourne, his long-standing adviser and confidante. She was almost 40 years Byron's senior, but the nature of their relationship is poignantly revealed in a letter he addressed to

Lady Blessington in which he writes, "Lady Melbourne, who might have been my mother, excited an interest in my feelings that few young women have been able to awaken."

Of Augusta, was it fact or fantasy? Though the evidence seems pretty conclusive that the relationship was incestuous, who can be absolutely sure? The fact remains that he was more deeply and constantly in love with her than with any other woman in his life. Apologists for Augusta, working, however, from far different premises, maintained that her attitude towards Byron was that of a mother. I believe them to be right. For Byron she was a mother figure par excéllence. She was older than he, his sole remaining female blood relative, the co-inheritor of the Byronic heritage. She was sympathetic, understanding, affectionate, and loyal. It is, to me, understandable, that, despite the sure knowledge that he was committing social suicide, he was compelled irresistibly to continue his association with her. He says in his profoundly moving *Epistle to Augusta*:

> For thee, my own sweet sister, in my heart
> I know myself secure, as thou in mine;
> We were and are – I am, even as thou art –
> Beings who ne'er each other can resign;
> It is the same, together or apart –
> From life's commencement to its slow decline
> We are entwined – let Death come slow or fast
> The tie which bound the first endures the last!

It is worthy of note and gratifying to me that Bertrand Russell in his perceptive account of Byron in his *History of Western Philosophy* arrives at virtually the same conclusion. He writes, "His shyness and sense of friendlessness made him look for comfort in love-affairs, but as he was unconsciously seeking a mother rather than a mistress, all disappointed him except Augusta."

It is not for me to pronounce judgment on Byron either in respect of his relationship with Augusta, or in respect of the wider social implications of his abnormal behaviour. That would be encroaching on the field of ethics and morals, which is not my province. My brief is to offer an explanation, not an excuse, for what he was and for what he did.

Byron himself was acutely aware of his heritage in which wickedness played such a prominent part. He considered that he was inescapably predestined by an evil fate, perhaps in a Calvinistic way by the Almighty, to follow his ancestors down the primrose path to the everlasting bonfire. But this may well be his rationalisation of inner forces of which he was consciously unaware. Furthermore, to accept such an explanation would be to negate entirely our present day understanding of psychodynamics. It is my contention – and I have been at pains to illustrate my thesis – that with all of us, as with Byron, life is a continuum and that things ill begun by the damaged seed of heredity are made worse by the poor soil of environment.

The child is father to the man: Childe Harold is father to Lord Byron. But, nevertheless, one can never be too sure. There are often times when paternity is called into question.

## BIBLIOGRAPHY

Quennell P, ed. *Byron, a self-portrait*. London: John Murray, 1936.
Marchand, L A, ed. *Byron's letters and journals*. London: John Murray, 1973.
Cecil D. *The young Melbourne*. London: Constable, 1940.
Howarth R G. *The letters of Lord Byron*. London: Dent, 1936.
Langley Moore D. *The late Lord Byron*. London: John Murray, 1961.
Maurois A. *Byron*. London: Bodley Head, 1963.
Origo I. *The last attachment*. London: Jonathan Cape and John Murray, 1949.
Coleridge E H, ed. *Poetical works of Lord Byron*. London: John Murray, 1905.
Quennell P. *Byron*. London: Duckworth, 1934.
Russell B. *History of western philosophy*. London: Allen and Unwin, 1961.

## GEORGE BERNARD SHAW: THE DOCTOR'S DILEMMA?

George Bernard Shaw's doctors might be excused for allowing him to slip through their fingers when, within five years of his centenary, he fell out of a tree and fractured his thigh. They had less excuse for having failed to ameliorate, let alone cure, his recurrent prostrating headaches; or for bungling the treatment of a necrotic condition of a bone in his ankle, so keeping him precariously balanced on crutches for an unnecessarily long time. Then, in late middle life, he developed a hydrocele, for which the doctors recommended surgery. Shaw declined. He sought treatment from an osteopath, who prescribed a daily dose of a sugar-like powder. As Shaw records them, the sequence of events was that in the course of the treatment he was awakened one night by what he thought was a burst hot water-bottle, but on investigation found that the hydrocele had discharged itself – and was cured. Coincidence? Probably. Shaw was in no way convinced, and, in any event, he preferred such pleasant coincidences to the knife. What may have been the most damning failure in Shaw's eyes was that, in spite of having been vaccinated, he contracted smallpox in the epidemic of 1881. Conceivably, then, his mistrust of doctors in general and of "serum therapists" in particular arose from his own personal experiences. My dynamically orientated colleagues might, however, with reason, attribute his hatred of all established authority, including that of medicine, to what he himself described as a "devil of a childhood" – for which his boss-eyed, drunken father and his cold fish of a mother must be held largely responsible.

Ignorance never prevented Shaw from pronouncing on matters about which he felt passionately; and he felt passionately about the "serum doctors" and their animal experiments. As a vestryman and later councillor of the borough of St Pancras he campaigned unceasingly for better sanitation, including in his brief the provision of free public lavatories for women. Against all the evidence he maintained that dirt and not germs was responsible for infectious and contagious disease. He went further. Inspired, it is said, by an incident he witnessed in Sir Almroth Wright's laboratory at St Mary's Hospital, he wrote a play which permitted him to inveigh against doctors and their practices. The play was *The Doctor's Dilemma* and was first produced in 1906.

I first saw the play as a schoolboy in Leeds. The visit of the Macdona Players, who toured Shaw's plays, was a major event in our provincial lives. For six (old) pence you could climb the staircase to the stars and have Jennifer Dubedat on Mondays and Eliza Doolittle on Fridays. For no extra charge you could play stage-door Johnny and collect her autograph, if the last tram home afforded you the time to wait. Later, much later, and for much more money, I saw the West End production at the Haymarket (I think) with the irresistible Vivien Leigh (I'm sure) as Jennifer. Then, in April 1975, at the Mermaid Theatre, Puddle Dock, by courtesy of Sir Bernard Miles, one of the theatre's great folk-heroes, I was privileged to go to a revival. Not only this, but during rehearsal I had the rare opportunity of sitting in and watching the infinite patience and skill, not to mention hard labour, that the craftsmen-actors and actresses at the Mermaid put into what they were about.

The play in some respects is an enigma. Is it a comedy or a tragedy? The handbill advertises it as the former; the subtitle to the text describes it as the latter. Is it an exhibition of high human drama, or corny melodrama? Is it a study of death, as personified by the consumptive Louis Dubedat, a totally amoral artist of rare talent? Or does it illustrate Shaw's preoccupation with the Life Force (whatever that may be), of which sex in the person of Jennifer, the artist's wife, and later widow, is merely an instrument? I just don't know; but it is, nevertheless, an experience not to be missed to see how Shaw with his consummate skill as a dramatist can play ducks and drakes with one's emotions and intellect.

These imponderables are, as we say in the trade, the latent content. The play's manifest content is as plain as a pikestaff. The plot is the dilemma, the doctor's dilemma – that is, the choice that has to be made by Sir Colenso Ridgeon, a thinly disguised representation of Sir Almroth Wright, between giving his magic anti-tubercular serum to Dubedat and so preserve a genius; or to another consumptive, Dr Blenkinsop, a dour, dull, desperately poor but sincere and honest general practitioner who yearns to dedicate his life to a state medical service. But the choice is not a free one because Ridgeon has fallen in love with Jennifer. In the course of the play Shaw sets up the medical establishment as a coconut-shy, which he then proceeds to demolish. There is Sir Ralph Bloomfield Bonington, an eminently successful and fashionable physician, but a shyster, who latches on to Ridgeon's researches with no understanding at all of what they are about. Then there are Dr Leo Schutzmacher, who achieves riches as a sixpenny doctor by exploiting the credulity of the poor in the same way as Sir Cutler Walpole, a well heeled surgeon, exploits the hypochondriasis of the rich. Presiding over the charade is Sir Patrick Cullen, Ridgeon's mentor and now an elder medical statesman, an expatriate Irishman, who, needless to say, is the mouthpiece for Shaw's own vitriolic cynicism. But in typical Shavian fashion it is the amoral Dubedat who does all the moralising and serves as the vehicle for most of the intellectual gymnastics, paradoxes, and double-talk. "I don't believe in morality. I'm a disciple of Bernard Shaw," Dubedat is made to say.

In one respect it is very probable that Shaw did influence the course of social and medical history. He was as bitter an enemy of private medicine as he was a staunch advocate of a salaried national health service, and his power and influence as a leading Fabian in the days before the Lloyd George Act of 1911 cannot be underestimated. What would he have thought of today's doctors' dilemmas – which unless resolved, and resolved quickly, threaten to tear the National Health Service and the medical profession to pieces? There are categorical statements in the preface to the play which are so apropos as to be irresistible. The preface begins: "It is not the fault of our doctors that the medical service of the community as at present provided for, is a murderous absurdity." Splendid! Later he declares: "By making doctors tradesmen we compel them to learn the tricks of the trade." Even better! And then, there is one in the eye for the other side as he proclaims: "It must not be hastily concluded that this [a public health service] involves the extinction of the private practitioner."

I don't guarantee, of course, that these quotations are entirely in context. But if Shaw can play both the devil's disciple and advocate, and cite the scripture for this purpose, why in Heaven's name can't I?

# JAMES JOYCE AND HIS IMPOSSIBLE HEALTH

James Joyce might have become a doctor. In fact, he made an attempt to acquire medical qualifications in Dublin and Paris, but in both centres of learning he gave up almost before the ink of his enrolment was dry. In this respect he fared even worse than his father, who at least got as far as taking some of his medical examinations although he failed to pass them.

Nevertheless, the younger Joyce managed to pick up a quite extraordinary familiarity with medical practice, but from the wrong end of the stethoscope or, more precisely, of the ophthalmoscope. So much was this the case that by 1919 he could write to his devoted patroness, Harriet Weaver: "I ought to apologise for my impossible health which so often obliges me to appear discourteous." There was worse to come as he grew older and the catalogue of his medical misfortunes lengthened.

At various times of his life he was treated for arthritis, conjunctivitis, and urethritis. (There is a possibility that these symptoms were those of Reiter's disease.) During the last year or so of his life it seems certain that he suffered severely from a chronic duodenal ulcer, which in January 1941 perforated with fatal results. But, to use a mixed metaphor which would have commended itself to Joyce himself, his Achilles' heel was his eyes. He was myopic from birth, but this was the least of his optical troubles. Superimposed on this defect he contracted just about every ophthalmological complication in the book, so that his eyes must have displayed a veritable museum of pathology. Between 1917 and 1930 he underwent no less than 25 operations for, inter alia, glaucoma and iritis. At times the pain was unendurable; at times he was totally blind.

To cap the list of physical disabilities, mention must be made of his impossible dental health. "My mouth is full of decayed teeth and my soul of decayed ambition," Joyce wrote as early as 1906. In 1923 what teeth he had left were removed and dentures fitted.

But was Joyce's mental health as impossible as his physical and dental health? Much as one may object to an attempt to formulate retrospective diagnoses based on biographical and autobiographical data, the evidence points indisputably to some degree of mental imbalance, particularly towards the end of his life when he may have become overtly psychotic.

What is the evidence? There was more than a minor degree of predisposition in his family and previous personal histories. His father was a hopelessly improvident drunken profligate – unfortunate characteristics some of which his son himself manifested, though to a lesser degree. In a revealing moment of self-deprecation James described himself as "a man of small virtue, inclined to alcoholism." Owing to his father's financial collapse, James had to leave the rarefied and privileged atmosphere of Clongowes Wood College, the "Irish Eton" and, together with his nine siblings, accustom himself to a life of sordid, abject poverty. He eventually entered a Jesuit grammar school, where he became head boy but left under a cloud. It was at this time he lost his faith and renounced the Catholic Church.

It was about this time too that his life of dissolution began. In 1904, the year after his mother's death, he left Ireland, taking with him Nora Barnacle with whom he lived and by whom he had children "without benefit of clergy", although in 1931 the union was eventually regularised. Nora appears to have been his exact antithesis. She was uncultivated and naïve. "I guess the man's a genius, but what a dirty mind he has, hasn't he?" was her ingenuous assessment of her husband's literary ability. All these personal details of perhaps small individual importance do in the aggregate indicate a determination on the part of Joyce, for whatever reason, to spit in the eye of authority and convention.

Much later on in his life there are overt indications of serious mental imbalance. For example, he became irrationally impressed by coincidences. Thus, in 1939, when the Russians invaded Finland he connected the event in some mysterious way with the publication of *Finnegan's Wake*. Again, in 1935, at a time when he was deeply disturbed by his daughter's psychotic behaviour, Joyce became hallucinated for hearing. It is noteworthy that C G Jung, who in 1930 wrote a preface to the third edition of the German translation of

*Ulysses,* cited the work as an example of the schizophrenic mind. It was Jung, incidentally, who, together with other psychiatrists who examined Joyce's daughter Lucia, diagnosed her mental illness as schizophrenia. In this case, genetically speaking, had the rotten apple fallen far from the rotting tree?

Is there evidence in Joyce's writing of serious mental disturbance? Again, it would be folly to be too categorical. Nevertheless, there appear to have been significant changes in the texture of his writing as he got older. It is difficult to reconcile, say, *Chamber Music* (1907), with its undoubted lyrical qualities and its ease of comprehension, with the obscurity of his later work. Not only is *Finnegan's Wake* (1939) incomprehensible to the average reader, including myself, but in addition the stream of consciousness technique and the total disregard of syntax renders it as unstructured and formless as is much modern music and art. To pile Pelion on Ossa, Joyce distorts the language itself in a way that some schizophrenics fragment spoken and written speech. This is nowhere better seen than in the jingling catalogue of nonsense characterised by neologisms and clang associations to be found in the penultimate section of *Ulysses*:

Sinbad the Sailor and Tinbad the Tailor and
Jinbad the Jailer and Whinbad the Whaler
and
Ninbad the Nailer and Finbad the Failer etc.
etc.

But was this bizarre writing spontaneous or contrived? Yet another letter to Harriet Weaver, written in 1934, confuses rather than clarifies the issue: "Perhaps I shall survive and perhaps the raving madness I write will survive and perhaps it is funny. One thing is sure, however, Je suis bien triste."

In the final analysis, was Joyce mad? He may have been: and again, he may not, as they say in Ireland. And does it matter? Not at all. Irrespective of his mental health, possible or impossible, Joyce's position as one of the most commanding literary influences of our time is assured.

# 20 Medical journalism

When once the itch of litherature comes over a man, nothing can cure it but the scratching of a pen. – SAMUEL LOVER, *Handy Andy*

When can the medical writer claim with any degree of legitimacy to have joined the inky trade as a professional? The answer, I suppose, is from that russet-mantled morn when the first request from an editor to write something on his behalf plonks down on the doormat. The nature of the initial request, as with subsequent requests, can vary widely depending on what lies within the editor's gift. It may, for example, be a royal command for a leading article, a book review, or a report on a meeting or a symposium one has attended. And if one's early labours are crowned with success an invitation may be received to contribute a chapter for a multi-author book or, if the gods are in a particularly benevolent mood, to write a book as sole author.

But professionals, even medical journalists, cannot live by ink alone. They must be paid, and the sum the editor is prepared to pay is customarily written into the commissioning letter. A word of warning to those who aspire to join the ranks of medical journalists: there must be singularly few who can depend on their pen for a living. The vast majority are only able to supplement their income to a greater or lesser extent. As for myself, although I have earned a tidy sum over the years, I am firmly of the opinion, an opinion endorsed by my accountant, that as a cost-effective exercise it would have been more profitable to spend the time (not to mention the blood, sweat, and tears) in addressing envelopes on a commercial basis. The undeniable fact, however, is that I love doing what I am called upon to do and, blasé as I may have become with the passage of time, I still get a greater kick from seeing something I have toiled over "on the page" than I have ever received from champagne, or, with just a few exceptions, whatever else turns me on.

My own career as a medical journalist, if I have to be bound by the criteria I have laid down, began in 1966 when I was invited by the editor of the *British Medical Journal* to write a leader on the controversial subject of community care. I was flattered and not a little frightened at the prospect, but set to work immediately: the finished product under the heading, "Does the community care?" was published anonymously as a first leader on 17 September 1966. Since then I have written close on 50 leaders, almost all for the *BMJ*. Not long afterwards, I was asked to review a book, *The Construction and Government of Lunatic Asylums* by John Conolly, reissued with an introduction by Richard Hunter. This was to be the first of many such requests. Interspersed between leaders and book reviews have been contributions to its non-technical columns, such as Personal View and Materia non Medica.

I have not the slightest doubt that the opportunity to win my spurs as a medical journalist was thanks to the patronage of the *BMJ*. Work for other journals has followed so that for the past 25 years or so I have rarely been out of print. And never have I felt more fulfilled.

There is nothing like a leading article to concentrate the mind most wonderfully; and reviewing books is a way of keeping abreast of the literature and at the same time augmenting one's library, if not one's income. But the privilege and pleasure that I treasure beyond measure is to have contributed on a regular basis from 1967 onwards to *World Medicine* in the golden years of Michael O'Donnell's editorship. The main objective of this journal was to entertain, and to this end the editor gave his writers a free rein: the whole anatomy of humour could be dissected within the broad context of medicine. The opportunities afforded were limitless and were seized upon with gusto by those privileged to contribute. *World Medicine* in its time must have been the most widely read and the most enjoyed medical journal in the

UK and I still mourn its premature and, as far as I am aware, unnecessary demise.

As a last indulgence I propose to offer an article which was published in *World Medicine* on 10 August 1977:

## MORTAL IN A WHITE COAT

Would the history of the world have had to be rewritten if Cleopatra's nose had been differently shaped, or just a few millimetres longer? For centuries philosophers have wrestled with this hypothetical question. I, in my egocentric way, have often pondered the pattern of my life had the shape and measurements of my lower abdomen been the same then as those that shame me today. There is a possibility that precisely nothing would have changed. Conversely, there is a better than evens chance that I would at some time have been whisked into hospital in the dead of night, bells ringing and lights flashing, as a surgical emergency.

The events of which I write occurred several light years ago when for a fleeting moment I was by definition an officer and a gentleman. It so happened that one morning, as I was drying myself after a bath, I happened to cough while glancing at my right groin, an exposure which was permitted me then, but is denied me now. To my horror a small but very definite bulge appeared. In order to convince myself that I was not hallucinated I repeated the performance several times, but the selfsame tell-tale bulge persisted in making itself seen and felt. "Common conditions occur commonly," I repeated to myself, reciting a catechism etched indelibly into my memory years before. Ergo: the chances were that the offending bulge was a hernia. But was I sure? I was not. From that moment on, the indignities of patientdom followed in quick succession.

As soon as I had recovered my aplomb I reported to the station sick-quarters and asked to see the duty medical officer, a pal of long standing. But the relationship was suddenly and mysteriously changed. I, by virtue of my imperfection, was now a patient while he remained the doctor, and as such held dominion over me.

"Go into a cubicle and strip off," he commanded.

Meekly and unhesitatingly I obeyed. He went through the accepted clinical examination. He confirmed that something was amiss but wouldn't commit himself further.

"Better see the surgeon at RAF Hospital X," he suggested while washing his hands with what seemed to me unnecessarily scrupulous care. I could have bitten my tongue, but spontaneously, almost reflexly, I replied, "Yes, sir."

There is nothing more socially levelling than an outpatient department. Airmen and non-commissioned officers with buttons like burnished gold mixed with commissioned officers with buttons of a duller hue. Democratically each awaited his turn to be summoned to the presence, the presence being that of one of London's leading surgeons transmuted "for the duration" into an officer of field rank. The waiting seemed endless. I toyed with a book I had brought with me, but such was my anxiety that the words were meaningless. The process of turning the pages, however, served, as the pages of antique magazines in doctors' and dentists' waiting rooms serve, as a cover for anxiety.

Eventually I was called and ushered into the presence. I stood, and was allowed to stand, to attention, thus establishing beyond all doubt the rank-order and the professional relationship.

"You're a trick cyclist, eh?" said the great man glancing at my documents. Of all the pejorative terms used to describe my humble calling this was the one that infuriated me most. My impulse was to spit in his eye, but remembering that it was more than likely that I would, ere long, be at the sharp end of his scalpel, I reined myself in.

"What seems to be the trouble?" he demanded rather than asked.

"Right inguinal hernia, sir," I replied promptly, trying desperately hard to re-establish my identity as a doctor. But my courage failed me and I added tentatively, "I think."

"You think; you're not sure," he sneered, squashing me like a fly. "Then we'll have to make sure, won't we?"

The routine was now familiar. He prodded and poked around while at his behest I coughed, or stopped coughing and turned first this way and then that way. He kept me in suspense as he went through the ritual hand-washing. Then, as he dried each ramrod finger separately and ostentatiously, he said: "If you were up for your surgery clinical I'd fail you."

"Why, sir?" I piped obsequiously.

"You've got a brace of 'em," he proclaimed with all the arrogance of certainty, "and the sooner you have 'em repaired the better."

"Thank you, sir," I stammered, gratitude being, in fact, the last sentiment I felt at the time.

A week later later I was admitted to RAF Hospital X and was told to report to the sister of Ward Y. She sat in her office, her gleaming starched white uniform, with shoes, stockings, and cap to match, giving her an impregnability as effective as a convent wall.

"You're the bilateral hernia for operation tomorrow," she remarked with cold, clinical detachment. I had no name, no number, no identity. I was a thing called a patient in for repairs. She gave me my briefing. I was to proceed to room Z to undress and wait to be "prepped". There was to be no smoking and, of course, no drinking. Were there any questions? she went on to ask. With measured politeness I replied that there were none and went on my way to my room just across the corridor.

Reading was hopeless. I found a programme of music on the wireless (sic). The BBC, with an insensitivity bordering on the callous, was broadcasting a movement of Beethoven's Piano Sonata in A flat, op 26, "Sulla Morte d'un Eroe". I switched off and tried to lull myself into a trance-like state. How long I lay on my bed I've no idea, but some time later the first of a procession of aides appeared. He was the barber, a leading

179

aircraftsman (for collectors of misnomers I offer this one for free), who had come to give me the ceremonial shave. With extraordinary expertise he, in no time flat, cleared the undergrowth from the bathing trunk area leaving it looking as naked and as vaguely obscene as a plucked Christmas turkey. There followed other aircraftsmen, leading and otherwise, who, with commendable efficiency, did what they had to do according to their calling. But there was none of the chit-chat, none of the camaraderie common between doctors and ancillaries working on the same side of the fence. In spite of the sleeping pill, taken under protest, I slept badly and was restless and apprehensive, a state of unease relieved only by the sweet oblivion of the intravenous anaesthetic given me in my bed next morning.

At that time, following an operation such as I had had, it was considered mandatory to remain in bed for a full 14 days. Any movement was discouraged, so for that period I regressed to a state of almost total infantile dependency. I enjoyed it not at all and counted the days, and then the hours, until I could escape the thrall of patientdom. Fourteen days exactly after the operation, I decided to bridge that great gap of time between infancy and adulthood, between being a patient and being a doctor, with one leap. Throwing the bedclothes off the bed I leapt to my feet – and promptly fell flat on my face. In falling I brought down a standard lamp and a bedside table on which rested my breakfast tray. The noise of the crash brought pairs of helping hands rushing to my side. Ignominiously I was hoisted on to my rubber legs and led like a stumbling child back to bed. As they retreated through the door into the corridor I overheard one orderly say to the other: "Pranged his bloody bike that time and no mistake. Bloody fool. Ought to have his bloody head read."

The commotion had not escaped the notice of the inner sanctum. The ice-maiden stormed in to begin her harangue. The precise words she used escape me, but the content was that doctors are doctors, and patients are patients, even if they are doctors. It was a bravura performance which gained momentum as it proceeded. Then, drawing herself up to her full 5 ft 1 in, she delivered her last lines. With a dramatic intensity worthy of a Bernhardt or a Duse she declaimed: "Doctors, let me tell you, are only ordinary mortals in white coats." There she paused and slowly, slowly, her expression and her voice thawed. "Dammit, I should know. I'm married to one," she added, almost cooingly.

# 21  A late flowering

As a doctor, and in particular as a psychiatrist, I have been privy to the innermost secrets of some of my patients, secrets not confided to their most intimate friends, or even to their spouses. And given the opportunity, I could a tale unfold which, in many instances, would lend substance to the belief that, oftentimes, truth is far, far stranger than fiction.

For myself, I have, fortunately perhaps, never had to swap roles and expose myself to the same sort of self-revelatory examination to which I have subjected others. As I have made clear in earlier chapters, I have not laid and am never likely to lay myself down on the expensive couch of omniscience either as a learning, or as a therapeutic experience. I don't know, therefore, how I would be assessed by others, neither, lacking the necessary will or capacity for self-analysis, have I any clear idea how I would assess myself.

But this I do know: I am in essence a very private person, and for this reason I could never bring myself to write an autobiography that would come within a mile of telling the whole truth and nothing but the truth. I would not, even if I could, write une histoire amoureuse. Suffice it to say that I have had relationships of varying duration and importance. And yet, deep down, I had always entertained the romantic hope that, somewhere, at some time, I would meet someone who would bring depth, permanence, even meaning, to my life.

With each succeeding year the odds against the realisation of my hopes lengthened until, when I had passed my half century, any bookie would have given you a hundred to one – or more. But not for the first time have I confounded the bookies. What upset their calculations on this occasion was their failure to take into account the possibility, rare as it may be, of what the French in their romantic wisdom term le coup de foudre, a phenomenon which does to the emotions what a well delivered blow to the chin from Mike Tyson does to the consciousness.

The setting in my case was not quite as exotic as the Ponte Vecchio in Florence as with Dante, or the ballroom of the Capulets' palazzo in Verona as with Romeo. It was in fact the very English Surrey home of Naomi and Sidney Rosenberg, he not only my oldest friend but my dentist, who by some miracle of conservation has kept a full set of teeth in my head.

The occasion was the 21st birthday party of David, then a Guy's medical student. He was the eldest of their three sons, all of whom I had known since birth and to whom I was, as indeed I remain, "Uncle Henry". Among the guests I knew would be there was a classmate of David's, Anna-Maria (Maria) Tihanyi, about whom I had heard a good deal, enough to excite my curiosity more than somewhat. I knew, for example, that she was born in Budapest and that as a child, together her with mother and younger brother, she had been spirited out of Hungary by an underground American organisation to join her father in what was then Rhodesia. There she had had an outstanding academic career and had been accepted by Guy's as a medical student on her record and without interview.

Attending the party was a bevy of highly desirable, nubile, mini-skirted dolly birds, most of them Guy's medical students or nurses accompanied by their boyfriends. There were just a few who were unattached, or had become unattached follow-ing lovers' tiffs, and with them I chatted in a benignly avuncular way. It wasn't until quite late in the proceedings that I was introduced to a vivacious, violet-eyed brunette whom I immediately recognised as Maria; or was the recogni-tion due to the fact that she fitted the subject of some deep-seated, long-nurtured fantasy? Whatever the reason, the thunder rolled.

Any romantic aspirations I allowed myself to entertain at the time were reinforced some weeks later when we were both weekend guests of the Rosenbergs. Thereafter our courtship –

for that is what ensued – must rank as one of the most bizarre in recorded history. What put a brake on the natural development of such a relationship was the disparity in our ages: there was a gap of a whole generation between us. Nevertheless, we continued to meet and what fostered our relationship was a mutual interest in the history of medicine. We were both members of the Osler Club and the section of the history of medicine of the Royal Society of Medicine.

Never have I attended meetings with such regularity. We contrived to sit next to each other and went so far as to shatter convention by holding hands when the lecturer obligingly darkened the hall to show his slides. Similarly, I recall a formal dinner of the Osler Club in the great hall of the Society of Apothecaries when I ate my way through the menu with one hand, the other being engaged in surreptitiously pressing Maria's hand under the table. Never, I reckon, have these ancient timbers been put to better use.

So in its own idiosyncratic, stop-go fashion the affair developed until ultimately there seemed no further point in arguing with the inevitable. We were married; not once, but twice. The first was a civil wedding on 27 July 1973 in the register office in Epsom, and the second, a religious ceremony, on 9 December of that year in the synagogue in Bulawayo, Rhodesia, where Maria's parents still lived.

Every marriage if it is to have any chance of success must have its strategy. In our case it was decided that, come what may, we must continue our careers – a decision easy enough for me to carry out, but one offering almost insuperable difficulties for Maria. She was at that time an anaesthetics registrar at Guy's and later at the Queen Victoria Hospital, East Grinstead. We had made our home initially in my bachelor flat in Epsom, which for Maria meant long journeys in all weathers at all hours to and from London or East Grinstead. It was tough going, taking into account that, in addition to her demanding job, she had to continue to swot for the final FFARCS, not to mention the most arduous of all the jobs she had taken on, namely, the duties of a housewife and a hostess. But her heroic efforts soon began to pay dividends. In March 1975, at the first attempt, she passed her final fellowship examination and was appointed senior registrar at Guy's. In 1977, a vacancy arose for a consultant post at the Epsom District Hospital, within walking distance of our flat. She applied, and as is her wont on such occasions, she required only one bite at the cherry.

As Maria's career as a consultant in the NHS was about to begin, so mine was coming to an end. In November 1976, having reached the age of 65, I retired, but as I have already explained (chapter 14), only a very little grass was allowed to grow under my feet before I began a second career as a consultant forensic psychiatrist.

However, so as to put the cardinal events in my life into some sort of perspective, or, perhaps more to the point, to illustrate yet again my apparently limitless capacity to make haste slowly: in the year of my retirement from the NHS, our first child, Aron, was born, to be followed three years later by the birth of our daughter, Rebecca.

The advent of the children brought an entirely new dimension into my life: a new learning process began from scratch. Perforce, I had to make my contribution to the feeding, bathing, and nappy changing of the infants. The last of this catalogue I found the most difficult: the nappy pin, I discovered, could easily be classified as an offensive weapon. How many times the unfortunate, wriggling, screaming child was impaled I don't know, neither do I know how many infected puncture wounds of the pulp of my left thumb I sustained. What I do know is that I regarded the introduction of the disposable, self-adhesive nappy with blessed relief and hailed it as the greatest scientific advance since the discovery of the wheel.

Apart from learning the skills of the nurserymaid I found that at the same time I had enrolled in a course for the intensive study of developmental psychology. This as it progressed, convinced me that anyone who has not been a parent cannot possibly consider himself fully equipped to practise adult psychiatry. At various stages as my children developed I noted, always with interest, often with alarm, their fetishes, their obsessional rituals, their tics, their temper tantrums, their "safety" objects, be it a tattered, shredded remnant of a blanket, a one-eyed, moth eaten "teddy", or one of an infinite assortment of personal totems.

There were times when I felt I might seek the opinion of colleagues who were specialists in the field. I desisted for reasons mainly of personal pride. It's just as well I did for the simple reason that, as each of these seemingly neurotic symptoms were in turn discarded, I came to the realisation that they were normal reactions and were par for the course for the obstacle race which the process of growing up represents.

It has been a tough course, one which I am far from having completed, but the one vital lesson I have learnt is that the raising of children is the most joyful, the most fulfilling job in the world, and yet, at the same time, it is the most difficult and responsible. For the wise, there are no absolute rules, save only one, which is that an ounce of common sense is worth a ton of book knowledge. This lends weight to the adage that so many of our children and young adults today are not so much pock-marked as Spock-marked.

An over-riding concern of any caring parent lies in the education of his, or her, children, and, as an extension of this concern, the degree to which he, or she, can complement, or supplement, their formal schooling. Very early on I was forced to the conclusion that I was quite incapable of contributing in a pedagogic way to the educational process for the simple reason that for me to pass a single GCSE subject, let alone an A level, at any level, is today an impossibility. The only option left was to concentrate my efforts on attempting to teach them how to learn. To this end I have instructed them in the use of libraries, dictionaries, and reference books. More importantly, perhaps, I have tried to instil in them a love of language and of the liberal arts wherein lies the real embodiment of culture. The same could be said of foreign travel; and if nothing else, my children are exceedingly well travelled. Maria and I share the same wanderlust, and the problem of what to do with the children when we travel abroad has been solved by the simple expedient of taking them with us.

To what extent I have succeeded in helping in the education of my children, in a general or in a particular way, is impossible for me to judge. What I am sure of, however, is that in certain respects I have failed, and failed miserably in my attempts to persuade them to share certain of my beliefs, beliefs to which I subscribe with passion. These are, for example:

1   That there was life before the "telly".

2   That silence is, or can be golden, by which I mean the occasional blissful respite from the relentless, pounding cacophany of "pop" music.

3   That food can be something other than a vehicle for tomato ketchup.

# Epilogue

I became, as my readers will have gathered, a doctor not by choice, and a psychiatrist faute de mieux; all in all, not the most propitious foundation on which to build a career. And yet it is only in psychiatry perhaps that it could have worked out as well as it has done. Psychiatry, as I discovered, spills over into so many other disciplines that it affords a golden opportunity for the dilettante – which is essentially what I am – to flourish.

But no matter what, I am in no way dissatisfied with the course my life has taken which, but for the throw of the dice, might have been so different.

# Index